# ICE CORES and the AGE of the EARTH

LARRY VARDIMAN, Ph.D.

First Printing 1993
Second Printing 1996
Third Printing 1999

**Ice Cores and the Age of the Earth**



Institute for Creation Research
P.O. Box 2667
El Cajon, California 92021

Library of Congress Catalog Card Number:
ISBN 0-932766-30-7



Printed in the United States of America

## ACKNOWLEDGEMENTS

This monograph is dedicated to my son, Daniel, who has traveled with me to the bottom of the Grand Canyon, to the top of Mount St. Helens, and to the glaciers at Mt. Ranier. We are exploring the world together.

I thank the many reviewers, both creationists and non-creationists, who have helped make this a better document, especially Gerald Aardsma, Michael Oard, Edmond Holroyd, Andrew Snelling, and Kenneth Cumming. Any errors still remaining are, of course, mine.

Data for Dye 3, Milcent, and Camp Century, Greenland ice cores were provided by the National Geophysical Data Center in Boulder, Colorado. A special note of appreciation is expressed for the extra assistance provided by the staff.

I thank Dr. Henry Morris and ICR for providing the opportunity and facilities to conduct the research supporting this monograph. Thanks are expressed to Marjorie Appelquist for final editing of the manuscript.

## TABLE OF CONTENTS

## LIST OF FIGURES

| FIGURE | TITLE | PAGE |
|---|---|---|

# CHAPTER 1

# INTRODUCTION

Located near the North and South Poles are vast sheets of ice which have accumulated over thousands of years in the frigid polar latitudes. Approximately 75% of all fresh water on the surface of the earth is trapped in solid form in polar regions.

The largest sheet of ice in the Northern Hemisphere is located on Greenland, centered near 75° north latitude (Fig. 1.1). A permanent ice sheet is not located at the North Pole because no continental land mass exists above sea level.

In the Southern Hemisphere a large ice sheet covers Antarctica, which is centered on the South Pole (Fig. 1.2). There is so much ice in the Antarctic ice sheet that if it all melted, the levels of the world's oceans would rise about 55 meters.

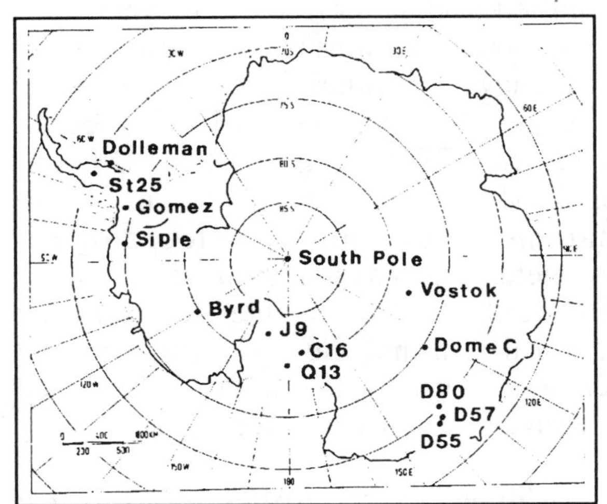


**Figure 1.2** *Ice core drilling sites on Antarctica (Clausen and Langway, 1989).*

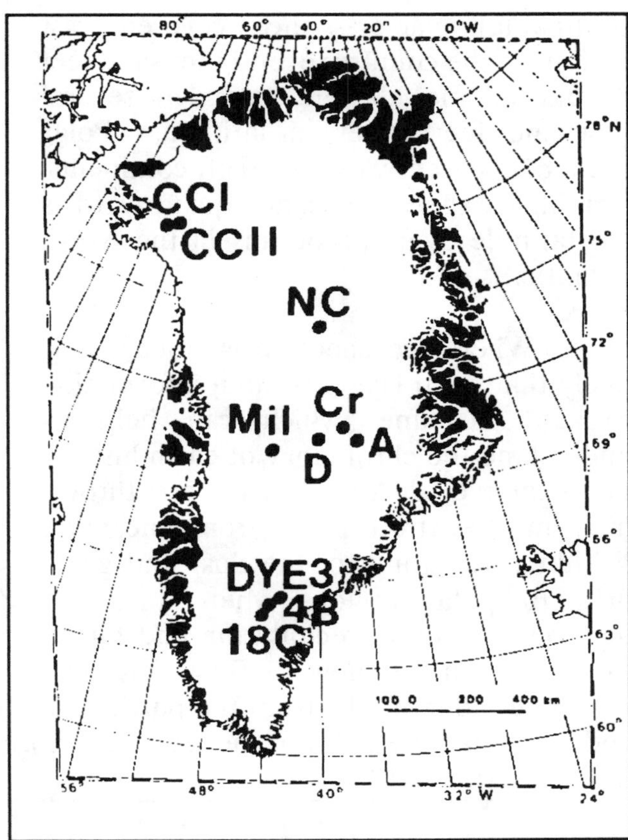


**Figure 1.1** *Ice core drilling sites on Greenland (Clausen and Langway, 1989).*

The maximum altitude of the Antarctic ice sheet reaches 4000 meters above sea level near the center of the large, circular continent. This ice sheet has profound influences on the atmospheric circulation in the Southern Hemisphere and characteristics of the precipitation.

Smaller, but not unimportant alpine glaciers and ice sheets exist at high altitudes of mountainous regions all over the world. Some of these even exist in tropical regions.

There is undeniable evidence that polar ice sheets and continental and alpine glaciers were more extensive in the past. In some places such as the north central and northeastern portion of the U.S., continental glaciers once covered vast regions of the country several thousand feet deep. Alpine glaciers extended several thousand feet lower in altitude. Polar glaciers apparently extended off continents, forming ice shelves to as far equatorward as 45° latitude over the oceans in the North Atlantic.

Where ice sheets exist today, it is likely that deep layers contain information "frozen" in time, which can help us understand the chronology of earth history. For example, dust and gases are thrown high into the stratosphere from volcanoes. Within a year or two, the dust and gases drift to polar regions where they are incorporated into precipitation and fall to the surface in the snow. Many volcanoes have been identified from the particulate and acid characteristics of the ice (Fig. 1.3).

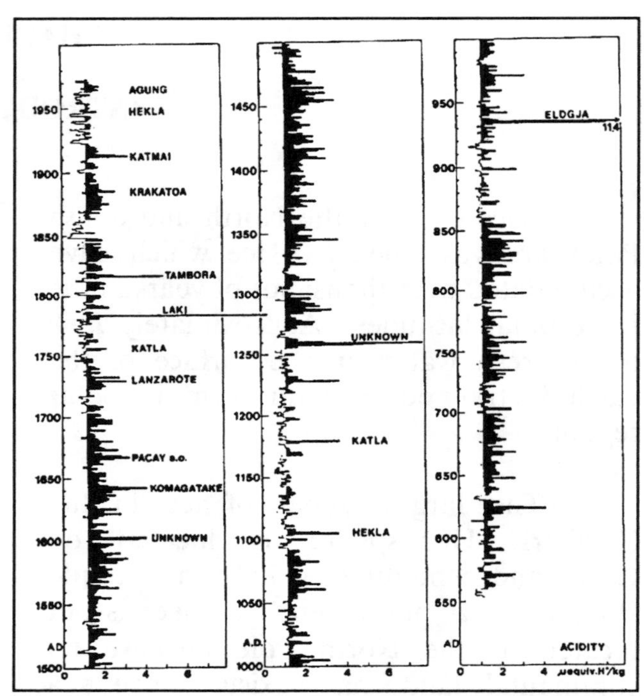


**Figure 1.3** ***Acidity versus depth for Milcent, Greenland correlated with volcanic eruptions (Hammer et al., 1980).***

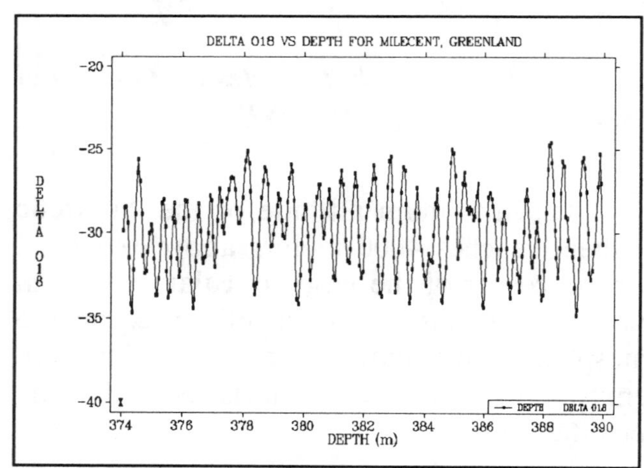


**Figure 1.4** ***Annual oscillations of the deviation in oxygen 18 ($\delta^{18}O$) from standard mean ocean water (SMOW) for Milcent, Greenland.***

Annual layers of precipitation can be identified back several thousand years into the past by oscillations in the characteristics of the snow, particularly $\delta^{18}O$, the deviation in oxygen 18 from standard mean ocean water (SMOW) (Fig. 1.4). Due to relationships between some of these characteristics and meteorological parameters, such as temperature, humidity, and winds, it is possible to construct historical chronologies of climate and weather. This technique has been used extensively to study the "Ice Ages."

Some characteristics of the ice sheets, such as the concentration of Beryllium 10 and Carbon 14, have been used to infer changes in the sun. Even bubbles of air trapped in the ice when it was formed have been used to estimate what the atmosphere may have been like in the past. Current increases in carbon dioxide measured at Mauna Loa, Hawaii have led to concerns about possible greenhouse warming. The trend of increasing carbon dioxide concentration was found to continue back in the record locked in ice at the poles (Fig. 1.5).

Continuous ice core drilling into polar glacier ice for scientific purposes was begun in 1956 in association with the International Geophysical Year (IGY). Surprisingly few ice cores have been obtained from various Greenland and Antarctic locations over the past thirty years. Only five ice cores have been recovered from depths of over 1000 meters (only three to bedrock), less than ten from depths of 300 to 500 meters, and only about two dozen from depths near 100 meters. After nearly a ten-year hiatus, teams from the U.S., France, and Denmark are again drilling cores in the Greenland ice sheet.

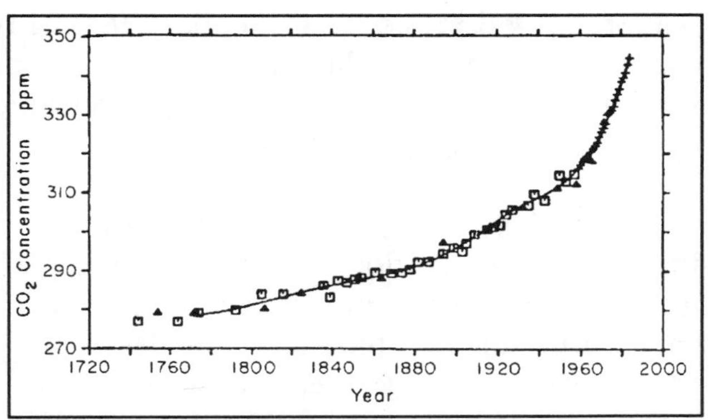


**Figure 1.5** ***Concentration of carbon dioxide for Siple Station, Antarctica (Khalil and Rasmussen, 1989).***

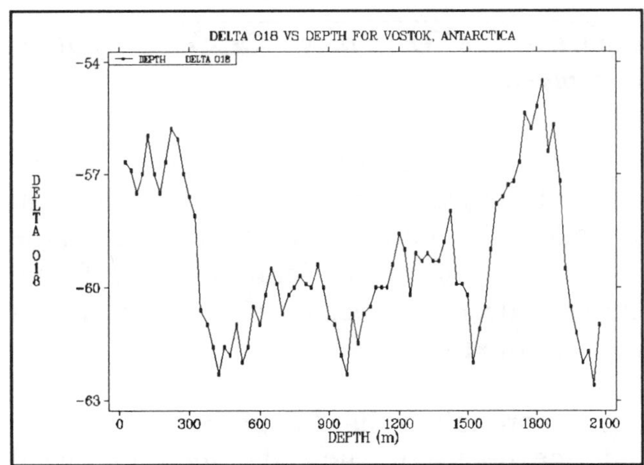


**Figure 1.6** ***$\delta^{18}O$ versus depth for Vostok, Antarctica.***

The processing and interpretation of ice cores takes tremendous amounts of money and effort. Most of the ice-core programs have been international in nature. Denmark, France, the Soviet Union, and the U.S. have been the main players in these efforts. Although results from the research have been published promptly by the principal investigators, the basic data have not been routinely available to other interested parties. Only within the last year or so have data been distributed to researchers outside the paleoclimatological community. This recent change is due to the establishment of the National Geophysical Data Center (NGDC) in Boulder, Colorado, which distributes data for a nominal cost to interested parties. Even this data center has had difficulty obtaining the raw data, particularly for Camp Century, Byrd Station, and Vostok.

1-303-832-2328?

ICR has been able to obtain data for several of the ice cores and expects to have access to others in the future. Until such time as all of the data are available, we are digitizing graphs of published results. Fig. 1.6 shows an example of digitized data from Vostok, Antarctica. Data obtained in this manner are limited in accuracy and resolution, but are adequate for interpreting and modeling many of the larger-scale features of earth history.

Published results of ice-core research have routinely reported that earth history has been recorded in the ice layers back tens of thousands of years, even to 160,000 years B.P. (before present). The last "Ice Age" supposedly ended abruptly about 10,000 B.P., and large variations in global temperature, $CO_2$, volcanic dust, and other climatic parameters occurred over the preceding 150,000 or so years.

In this report, I will attempt to show that this interpretation of long ages in the ice is a result of a preconceived view of earth history, rather than direct evidence of characteristics in the ice. It is true that direct evidence exists in the ice for annual layers which can be traced back several thousands of years. However, due to properties of the ice sheets (accumulation rates, firnification, and thinning), the identification of annual layers is limited to less than 10,000 years B.P. Firnification is the formation of compacted snow by melting, refreezing, and sublimation, in which characteristics of a snow layer are sealed off from effects above. Thinning is the gradual squeezing of ice layers as the accumulating weight of ice above forces ice below to move laterally. Below the level at which annual layering can be directly observed, models have been constructed to extend the chronology as far back as possible. Fig. 1.7 shows the $\delta^{18}O$ distribution in the Camp Century, Greenland core. The core below the Pleistocene-Holocene transition at about 1100 meters is claimed to extend to 160,000 years in the past.

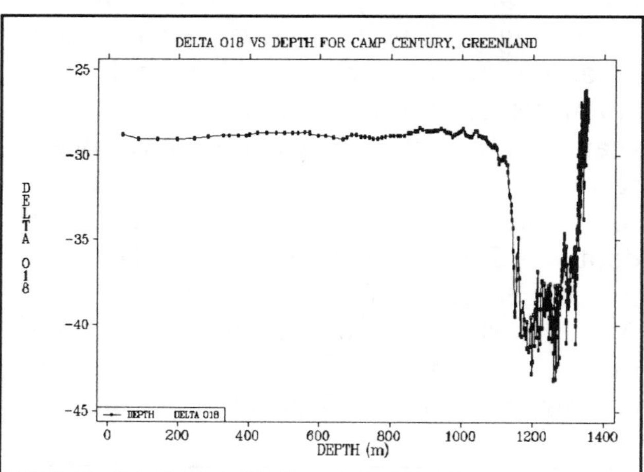


**Figure 1.7** ***$\delta^{18}O$ vs depth for Camp Century, Greenland.***

It is in constructing models to extend the geochronology that the preconceived view of earth history enters the interpretations. If one does not know the meteorological conditions in the past, and knowledge of these conditions is necessary to extend the ice core record back in time, it is common practice to assume that prior conditions were similar to those of today. The geological community uses a phrase for this uniformitarian assumption -- "The present is the key to the past."

In the case of ice-core research, the application of this principle is implemented by finding a relationship between the annual accumulation rate of snow onto the ice sheet and a variable which is readily observed in the ice sheet. The most-widely used variable in ice-core research has been the deviation in oxygen 18 from standard mean ocean water, $\delta^{18}O$.

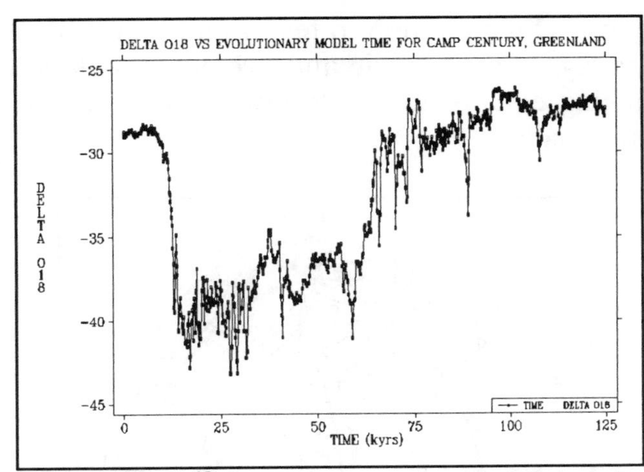


**Figure 1.8 $\delta^{18}O$ *versus long-age model time for Camp Century, Greenland.***

Over the recent period when annual layers of snow are detectable in the ice sheets, a good relationship has been found between $\delta^{18}O$ and temperature. Further, a good relationship has been found between atmospheric temperature and the accumulation rate of snow. Therefore, by combining these two relationships, a prediction of accumulation can be made, if $\delta^{18}O$ is known.

$\delta^{18}O$ is measured in ice cores all the way to the bottom. By calculating the accumulation rate from $\delta^{18}O$, integrating through the entire depth of the ice sheet, and considering other processes such as thinning, a chronology may be established. This is one of the processes which is used to arrive at estimates for the age of ice near the bottom of ice cores of 160,000 or so years.

However, if the meteorological conditions in the past were considerably different than they are today, such a model would not adequately represent the real chronology. For example, if accumulation rates near the bottom of the core were much greater than today, then the great ages found by the previous method would be invalid and much older than the actual fact. Fig. 1.8 shows the traditional interpretation of the Camp Century, Greenland core. Fig. 1.9 shows an alternative young-earth model interpretation. Not only does the young-earth model interpretation show a much shorter total time frame, but the fluctuations in $\delta^{18}O$ now become short-period oscillations.

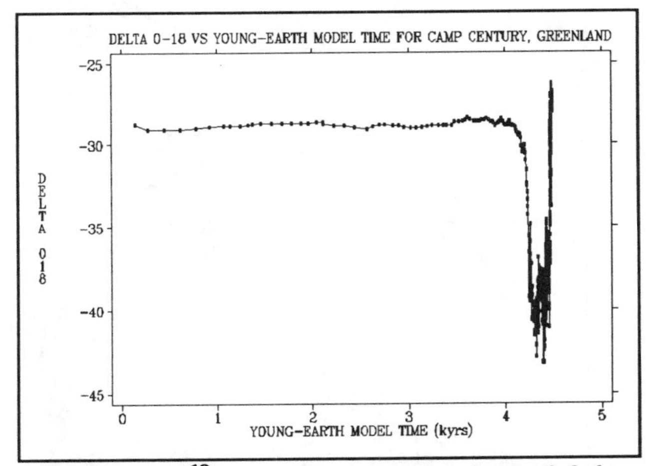


**Figure 1.9 $\delta^{18}O$ *versus young-earth model time for Camp Century, Greenland.***

In Chapter 5, an alternative model of ice-core chronology will be presented in detail, which is based on the expectations of ocean and atmospheric conditions following the Flood, as described in Genesis 6-9. The major feature of this model is the uniform ocean temperature from top to bottom and equator to pole immediately following the Flood. As the polar regions cooled following the Flood, approaching the temperature distribution observed today, large quantities of water vapor would have been evaporated from the warm oceans and deposited over cold polar regions. Precipitation rates would have been enormous initially, slowing to that observed today. Atmospheric and oceanic circulation patterns would have been driven by the changing equator-to-pole temperature gradient, causing precipitation patterns to fluctuate latitudinally.

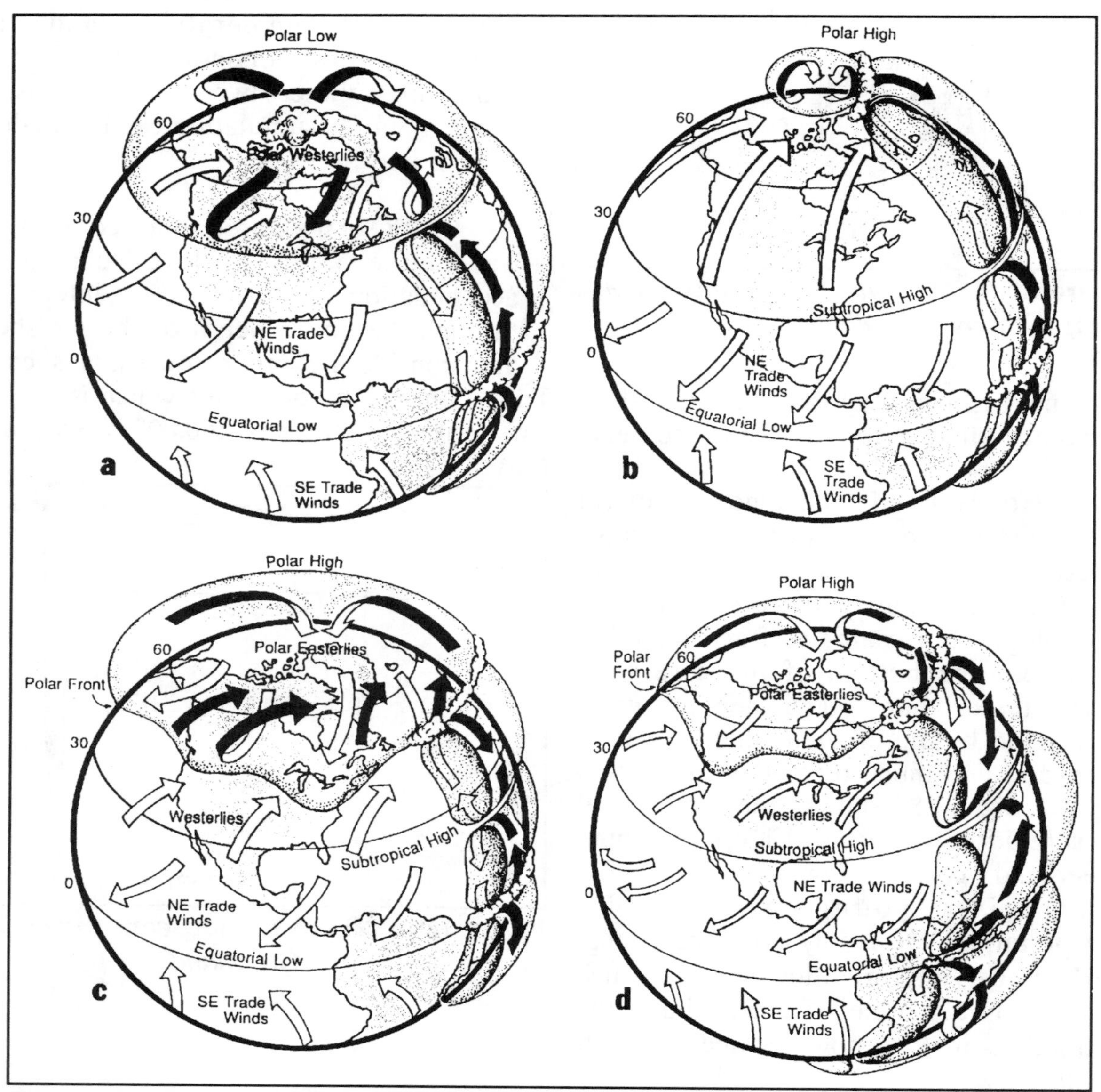


**Figure 1.10** *Global atmospheric circulation patterns after the Flood. a. Immediately after Flood. b. Within 100 years. c. At maximum extent of ice sheet. d. Today.*

A conceptual model of atmospheric conditions will be presented in Chapter 6 which is consistent with the theoretical dynamics of the general circulation, and explains the trend of $\delta^{18}O$ better than the standard model. Fig. 1.10 shows changes in the global atmospheric circulation following the Flood, as the oceans cooled and polar ice caps formed and then receded. One of the great puzzles of modern paleoclimatology is the explanation of the rapid increase in $\delta^{18}O$ at the Pleistocene-to-Holocene transition (Fig. 1.8). The alternative model presented in this report necessarily predicts a short transition period, and offers a plausible physical process for the transition. The physical process, explained fully in Chapter 6, is thought to be the rapid break-up of an ice shelf which grew equatorward to nearly 45° latitude, as a result of the high snowfall rates following the Flood. This ice shelf also caused the decline in $\delta^{18}O$ as the oceans cooled, and had a major influence on atmospheric and oceanic circulation patterns.

It is one thing to develop such a conceptual model, and another to demonstrate its validity from independent data. This report will not attempt to prove this conceptual model. Only general agreement with some of the available data will be attempted at this time. However, recommendations will be made regarding what studies should be conducted to validate the model. Of particular interest will be numerical experiments on a coupled atmosphere/ocean general circulation model. If general circulation patterns and precipitation rates can be found to be similar to those hypothesized in this report, I believe the model could be validated.

Ice cores, which until now seemed to be linked to long-age scenarios of earth history, appear to be a real tool for young-earth creationists. Because little or no information about global climatic conditions since the Flood appears in the Bible, it has been assumed that creationists could do little to counter the arguments of long periods of time for the "Ice Ages." However, with a straightforward inference about warm ocean temperatures caused by the Flood, it appears that a conceptual model of earth history since the Flood can be developed, which has the capability of being tested. This alternative model even seems to have the ability to explain several phenomena better than the traditional long-age model.

## CHAPTER 2

## DRILLING THROUGH HISTORY

### Introduction

The extraction of ice samples from deep within Greenland and Antarctic polar caps has less than a 40-year history. The first attempts were made in 1956 as part of the International Geophysical Year. Ten years later, the National Science Foundation, in association with the U.S. Army's Cold Regions Research and Engineering Laboratory (CRREL), invested in a major effort to drill completely through both the Greenland and Antarctic ice sheets.

Danish, French, and Russian teams have also drilled cores through these ice sheets, both in cooperative efforts and independent programs. Today, in 1992, two separate drilling efforts by the U.S. and European research groups are drilling cores through the deepest portion of the Greenland ice sheet. Less detail is available about the drilling procedures used by the other nations, so the U.S. efforts will be described in some detail. The equipment and procedures used by the drilling teams have also been improved for each new effort. However, the use of a modified electrodrill was found to be most successful at Camp Century, Greenland and Byrd Station, Antarctica in the 1960's. Its use will be described here.

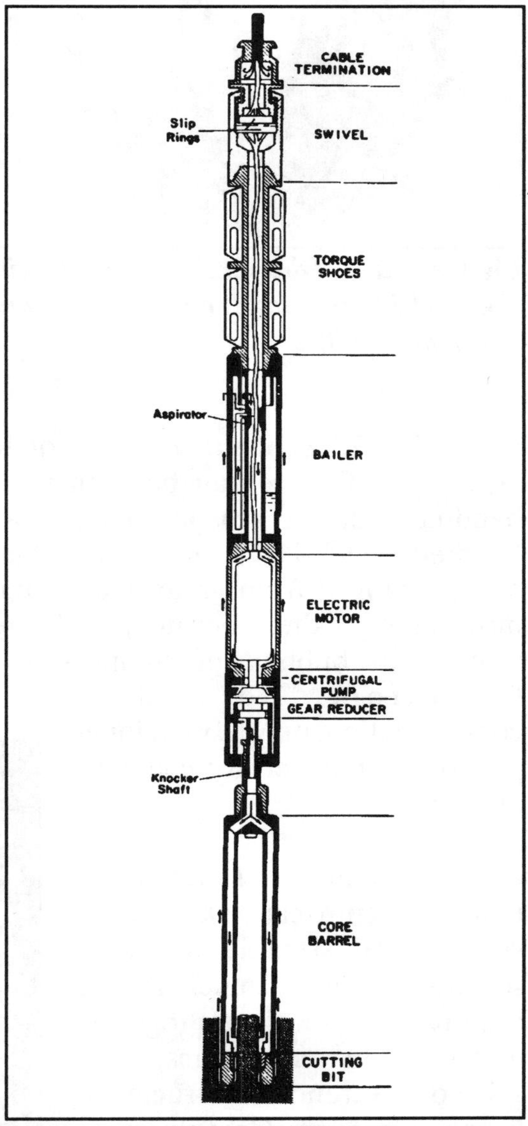


**Figure 2.1** ***Electrodrill used to extract ice cores at Camp Century, Greenland and Byrd Station, Antarctica (Ueda and Garfield, 1968).***

More detail on the equipment and procedures used in drilling through the Greenland ice sheet may be found in Ueda and Garfield (1968) and through the Antarctic ice sheet in Ueda and Garfield (1969). The complete report on Greenland core drilling by Ueda and Garfield (1968) is included as an appendix to this monograph.

**Figure 2.2** ***Diamond bit used with Electrodrill to extract cores (Ueda and Garfield, 1968).***

**Equipment**

Drilling was accomplished in Greenland and Antarctica with a cable-suspended, electromechanical, rotary coring Electrodrill shown in Fig. 2.1. The 80-foot-long drill was lowered up and down in the drill hole by a large cable, which also provided the electrical power to the drill. The drill cut a 4-1/4-inch- diameter core from the ice. Fig. 2.2 shows a diamond-studded bit used on the end of the drill to cut the cores. Twenty-foot sections of corings were drilled and removed by raising the entire assembly between advances. The cuttings produced by the bit were melted and cycled through the drill to aid in cooling the electric motor by a bailing assembly, which circulated ethylene glycol.

Fig. 2.3 shows an example of an ice core removed by such a drilling operation. The layering in the ice can be seen visually in the alternating dark and light bands. Such banding is due to seasonal melting and the presence of particulates. Cores are carefully handled to avoid contamination and kept at sub-zero tempertures to prevent melting. These cores removed from great depths must be allowed to stabilize for several months before movement to the laboratory. The release of pressure upon surfacing causes the ice to fracture as bubbles of compressed gases expand. When the cores finally reach the laboratory, to reduce contamination, only a small inner portion is removed for chemical analysis.

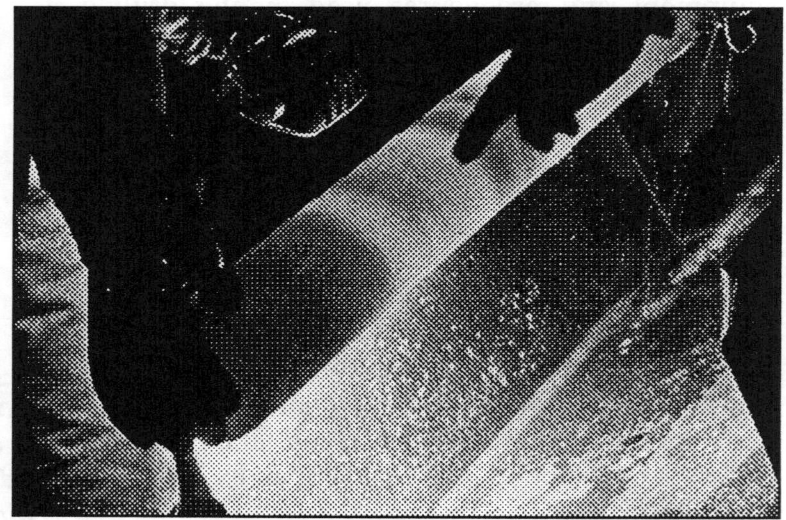

**Figure 2.3** ***Example of a core extracted from the Greenland ice sheet (Oeschger, 1967).***

Drilling cores a mile or more in depth can take several years, and sizeable teams of scientists and technicians are required to work closely together under adverse conditions. Fig. 2.4 shows a trench constructed at Camp Century, Greenland to protect the workers from the extreme cold and wind on the surface. Even out of the wind and cold, the conditions still are not pleasant. Temperatures must be maintained below freezing in the trench, and fumes from the ethylene glycol, power generators, electric motors, and lubricants can become concentrated.

**Figure 2.4** ***The trench in which the drill was operated below the ice surface at Camp Century, Greenland (Ueda and Garfield, 1968).***

**Operating Procedures**

A typical operating cycle in Greenland began with the lowering of the suspended drill into the hole (Fig. 2.5). At each appropriate section the drill was stopped, and lubrication of the gear section, lubrication of the motor section, and pumping of the required volume of concentrated glycol into the bailer was accomplished.

The drill was then lowered into the hole, initially by driving the hoist in reverse, and later by freewheeling the drive, as the added weight became great enough to pull out the cable. The descending drill was stopped three or four feet from the bottom of the hole and lowered at the desired drilling rate. The bit was started upon contact with the ice. It usually took 40-50 minutes to drill 15-20 feet of ice, at which time the drill was stopped and the core broken by lifting the cable slowly. Breaking a section of core from the ice beneath before lifting it to the surface occasionally became tedious, due to slippage of the core out of the barrel of the drill. A successful separation technique was developed.

**Figure 2.5** ***Workers preparing drill and bit before descent into the drill hole (Ueda and Garfield, 1968).***

After core separation, the drill was hoisted to the top of the hole, where an air wiper was used to remove the ethylene glycol. The bailer was emptied of the diluted ethylene glycol, and the barrel removed from the rest of the drill. Finally, the core was removed from the barrel and placed in cold storage (Fig. 2.6). The barrel was then reattached to the drill and lowered back into the hole, ready for another cycle.

**Figure 2.6** ***Removal of an ice core from the barrel of the drill (Ueda and Garfield, 1968).***

**Results**

In July 1966, a CRREL drilling team successfully penetrated the Greenland ice sheet at Camp Century, after drilling through nearly a mile of ice. On January 29, 1968, another CRREL drilling team successfully penetrated the Antarctic ice sheet at Byrd Station, after drilling through 7100 feet of ice.

Core recovery exceeded 99% of the depth drilled. With the exception of brittle and fractured cores from 1300 to 3000 feet, the overall condition of the core was good to excellent. Cores were 4-1/4 inches in diameter and from 10 to 20 feet long. At greater depths, unbroken lengths of 15 to 20 feet were not uncommon.

# CHAPTER 3

## INTERPRETING THE RECORD

Once an ice core has been successfully removed from an ice sheet, what is its significance? Is it possible to reconstruct the sequence of events which produced the characteristics evident in a vertical core thousands of feet long?

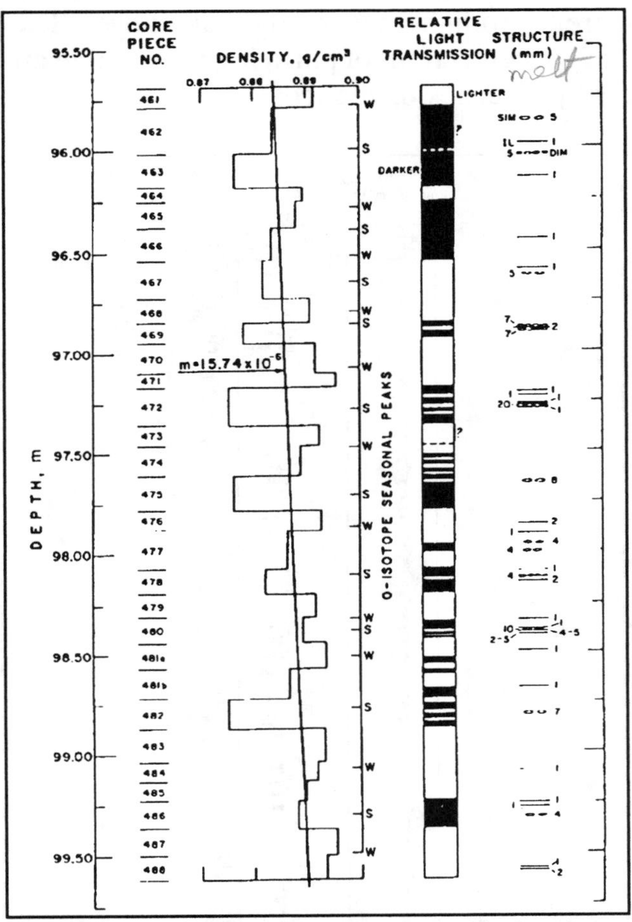


**Figure 3.1** ***Density and light transmission in an ice core from northwest Greenland (Langway, 1967).***

One of the most obvious characteristics evident in an ice core is the variable transparency of the ice along the core. As was seen in Fig. 2.8 some layers are fairly transparent, while others are opaque with a yellow or brown coloring. Fig. 3.1 shows a section of a core from 95 to 100 meters deep from northwest Greenland. The seasonal distribution of physical stratigraphic indicators is compared with oxygen isotope indicators. The seasonal distribution of $\delta^{18}O$ maxima (summer) and minima (winter) with depth compare favorably with the physical property measurements. The horizontal lines labeled "structure" to the right side of the figure represent melt layers.

Melt phenomena are postdepositional features and play a dominant role in polar stratigraphy. Warm summer surface temperatures create melt conditions and produce ice layers, ice wedges, and ice lenses, which form below the surface, sometimes after percolating downward as much as 2 meters (Benson, 1959). Depth hoar formation develops most favorably when a warm snow surface is quickly blanketed by a colder deposit. The new snow deposit restricts upward heat transfer and vapor migration, causing the vapor to condense at the interface. Under ideal conditions, a single distinctive depth hoar layer separates the summer/fall boundary, although these features may develop any time a steep temperature gradient exists (Schytt, 1958).

In the Dye 3 deep ice core, in central Greenland, distinct melt features and layers with fewer air bubbles have been observed and measured continuously on a light table to a depth of about 1500 meters, corresponding to a computed age of 5500 years B.P. A melt-layer study has the advantage of being a rapid method of obtaining independent proxy data on past summer climate, and it requires fewer assumptions to interpret the results than does the stable isotope method, to be discussed shortly.

Many other characteristics of an ice core may be observed as a function of depth. Most of these are not as obvious as the transparency to light seen by the naked eye. They require measurements with special equipment, of concentrations of particles, ions, stable and unstable isotopes, and electrical and mechanical properties of the ice.

The annual oscillations of electrical conductivity, oxygen isotope concentration, and microparticle concentration by light scattering are shown in Fig. 3.2 for Crête, in central Greenland. The oscillations have been observed to extend to great depth in the Dye 3 and Camp Century cores (Hammer et al., 1978). The limit to the identification of "annual" layers is generally considered to be 8,300 years B.P. (Johnsen et al., 1972). In the upper parts of the Greenland ice sheets these oscillations have been very accurately identified. One reason for such accuracy is the opportunity to cross check sharp peaks in a given variable with the effects of historic volcanic eruptions. Large volcanoes eject clouds of silicate microparticles and acid gases into the stratosphere which are subsequently incorporated into the precipitation of polar regions within a year or so of the eruption. Fig. 3.3 shows the acidity of annual layers from A.D. 1972 to 553 in the ice core from Crête (Hammer et al., 1980). Several well-known volcanic eruptions have been documented in the acidity record, e.g., Krakatoa (Indonesia, 1883), Tambora (Indonesia, 1815), and Laki (Iceland, 1783).

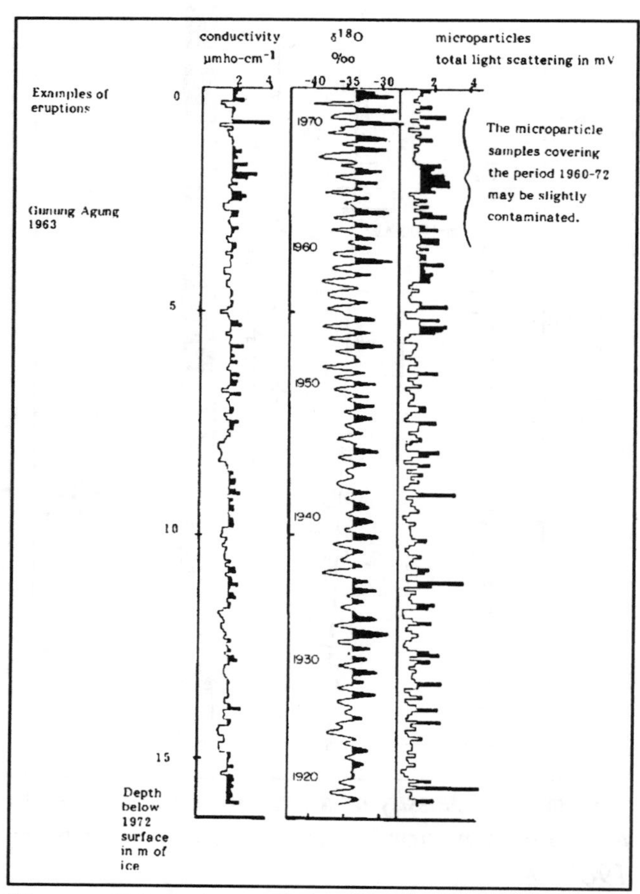


**Figure 3.2** ***Annual oscillations of electrical conductivity, $\delta^{18}O$, and microparticle concentration at Crête, in central Greenland (Hammer, 1989).***

Low-latitude eruptions generally show up with a time lag of about one year, due to the long travel time of the aerosols before deposition in Greenland. The layers of highest acidity coincide with internal reflection horizons in radio-echo soundings, and are recognizable all over Greenland. Most signals, particularly before A.D. 1600, are due to unknown eruptions somewhere in the Northern Hemisphere. The three strongest such signals were those in A.D. 1601-02, 1258-59, and 623-24. Before A.D. 900, the volcanism revealed in the Crête record cannot be ascribed to any known eruptions.

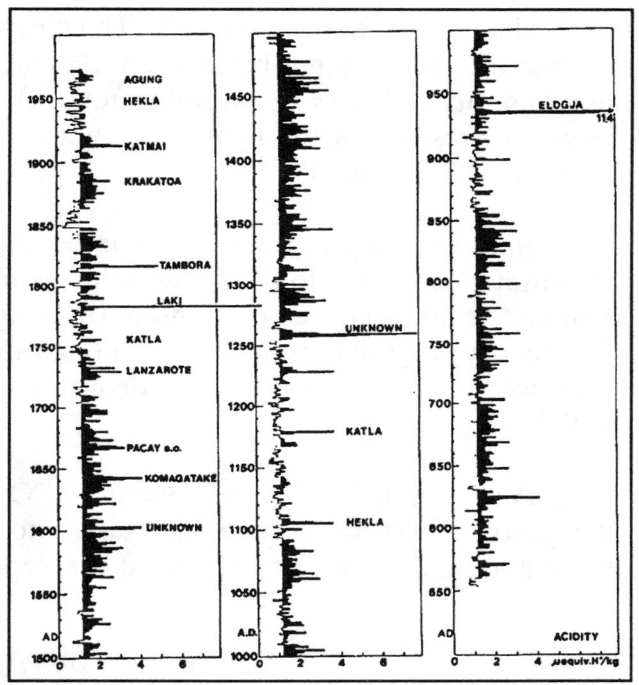


**Figure 3.3** ***Acidity in annual layers at Crête from 553 to 1972 A.D. Also indicated are historic and unknown volcanic eruptions (Hammer et al., 1980).***

The acidity technique has been applied to the Camp Century core, and was found to be similar to Crête, except near the bottom. The lower levels of the Camp Century core extend beyond that of Crête, and many unknown volcanic events were supposedly evident back to about 8000 B.P. The acidity technique could not be applied to the Camp Century core beyond 8000 B.P. because of the limited resolution of the electrodes. More importantly, the background concentration near the bottom of the core is higher in chemical element content by factors of 1.5 to 30. Concentrations are particularly high for potassium, magnesium, silicon, and calcium. High backgrounds cause the current between the electrodes to go to zero. There is some indication of periods of intense volcanism, but the resolution is too poor for good detail.

Although numerous characteristics of ice cores have been measured and have contributed to the understanding of the sequence of events which produced the ice sheets, the single most important variable has been $\delta^{18}O$. This is primarily due to the sensitivity of $\delta^{18}O$ to the formation temperature of snow.

The deviation of oxygen isotopes relative to a standard has been defined as:

$$\delta^{18}O = \frac{R - R_0}{R_0} \bullet 1000 \text{ ‰ } (per\ mil) \qquad (3.1)$$

where R is the ratio of $^{18}O$ to $^{16}O$ in a sample of interest and $R_0$ is the ratio of $^{18}O$ to $^{16}O$ in some reference standard. In the case of $\delta^{18}O$ in ice, $R_0$ is the ratio of $^{18}O$ to $^{16}O$ in standard mean sea water (SMOW). The measurement accuracy with the conventional mass spectrometer technique is better than .1‰ for $\delta^{18}O$. This corresponds to less than 1/600 of the variability of $H_2{}^{16}O$ in natural waters. One important reason for this variability is that the vapor pressure of the light component $H_2{}^{16}O$ is about 1% higher than that of $H_2{}^{18}O$ (Jouzel and Merlivat, 1984).

Initial cooling of water vapor in equilibrium with SMOW will result in a first-stage condensate (precipitation) of the same composition as SMOW. Further cooling and immediate removal of the condensate (Rayleigh condensation) will cause gradual depletion of the heavy components in the remaining vapor, and consequently in the precipitation. In other words, the lower the condensation temperature, the lower the $\delta^{18}O$ of the precipitation.

A very simplified model relating $\delta^{18}O$ and condensation temperature (Craig, 1961; Dansgaard, 1964), which does not take into account variable components at the source region and depletions in transit or at the deposition site, gives:

$$\delta^{18}O = 0.67T(^{0}C) - 13.7‰ \tag{3.2}$$

Attempts have been made to demonstrate the linear relationship between the mean annual surface temperature, T, and the mean $\delta^{18}O$ of the snowpack. Fig. 3.4 illustrates one such attempt with real snow on Greenland (Johnsen et al., 1989). A series of "warm" stations near the coast to "cold" stations near the center of Greenland were used to infer a temperature relationship like that of Eq. 3.2. Obviously, temperature is not the only factor influencing the fractionation of the oxygen isotopes. A full explanation not contained in Eq. 3.2 includes kinetic effects, both in nonequilibrium evaporation from the oceans (Merlivat and Jouzel, 1979) and in nonequilibrium sublimation from supercooled vapor to ice crystals at late stages in the cooling process (Jouzel and Merlivat, 1984). Furthermore, it is necessary to account for the temperature dependence of the isotopic fractionation during phase shifts (Majoube, 1971), the relative degree of condensation/freezing versus sublimation/freezing processes in clouds, and the source regions of the vapor (Petit et al., 1991).

Attempts to use general circulation models to reproduce the global distribution of $\delta^{18}O$ in precipitation have been successful in many respects, but so far these models have been unable to reproduce important features such as the seasonal variation in today's Greenland precipitation (Jouzel et al., 1987). This may be because such precipitation is formed by mechanisms not taken into account by the models. If such modeling cannot simulate today's observations, there is little likelihood that the paleoclimatic record has been accurately simulated.

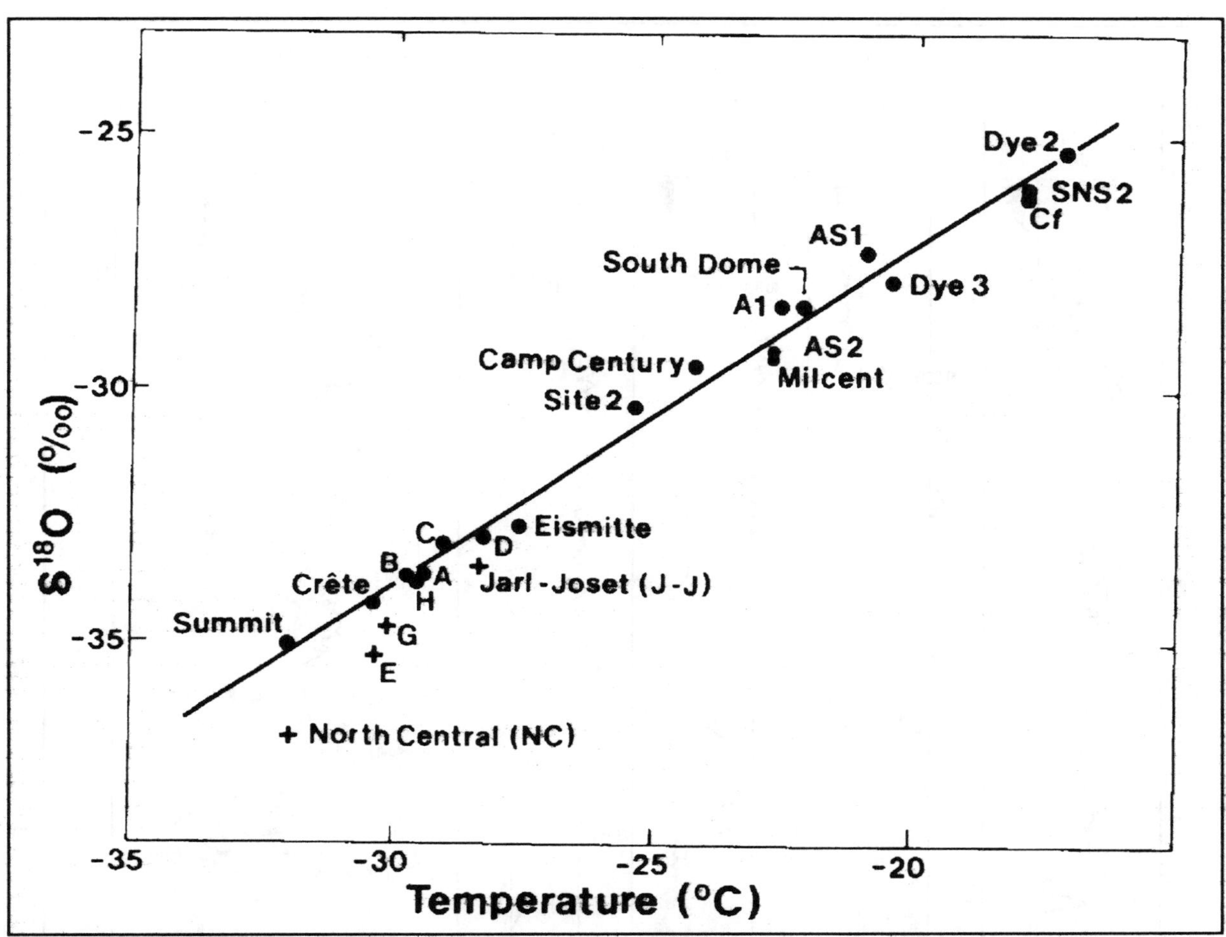


**Figure 3.4** ***$\delta^{18}O$ versus temperature as observed in precipitation on Greenland today (Johnsen et al., 1989).***

Nevertheless, the dependence of $\delta^{18}O$ on temperature expected theoretically and observed on an annual basis to great depths in Greenland ice cores has lent considerable credibility to attempts at interpreting past climates. When the $\delta^{18}O$ is relatively high, the average temperature is thought to be warm, and when it is relatively low, an "Ice Age" is hypothesized. Significant long- term or abrupt changes in $\delta^{18}O$ are interpreted to signal major climatic adjustments.

Fig. 3.5 shows the $\delta^{18}O$ record for the Camp Century, Greenland and Byrd Station, Antarctica ice cores. The plot for Camp Century is derived from an ice flow model to be described in Chapter 5. The plots for Byrd Station are derived from four different sets of assumptions using the same model in an effort to match the Camp Century and Byrd Station distributions. Similar shapes in the distributions of $\delta^{18}O$ in Greenland and Antarctica have led to the view that the worldwide climate entered the most recent ice age about 100,000 years B.P. During the latter part of the Pleistocene epoch, the polar regions and high-latitude regions of the earth were glaciated, reaching maximum coverage about 18,000 years

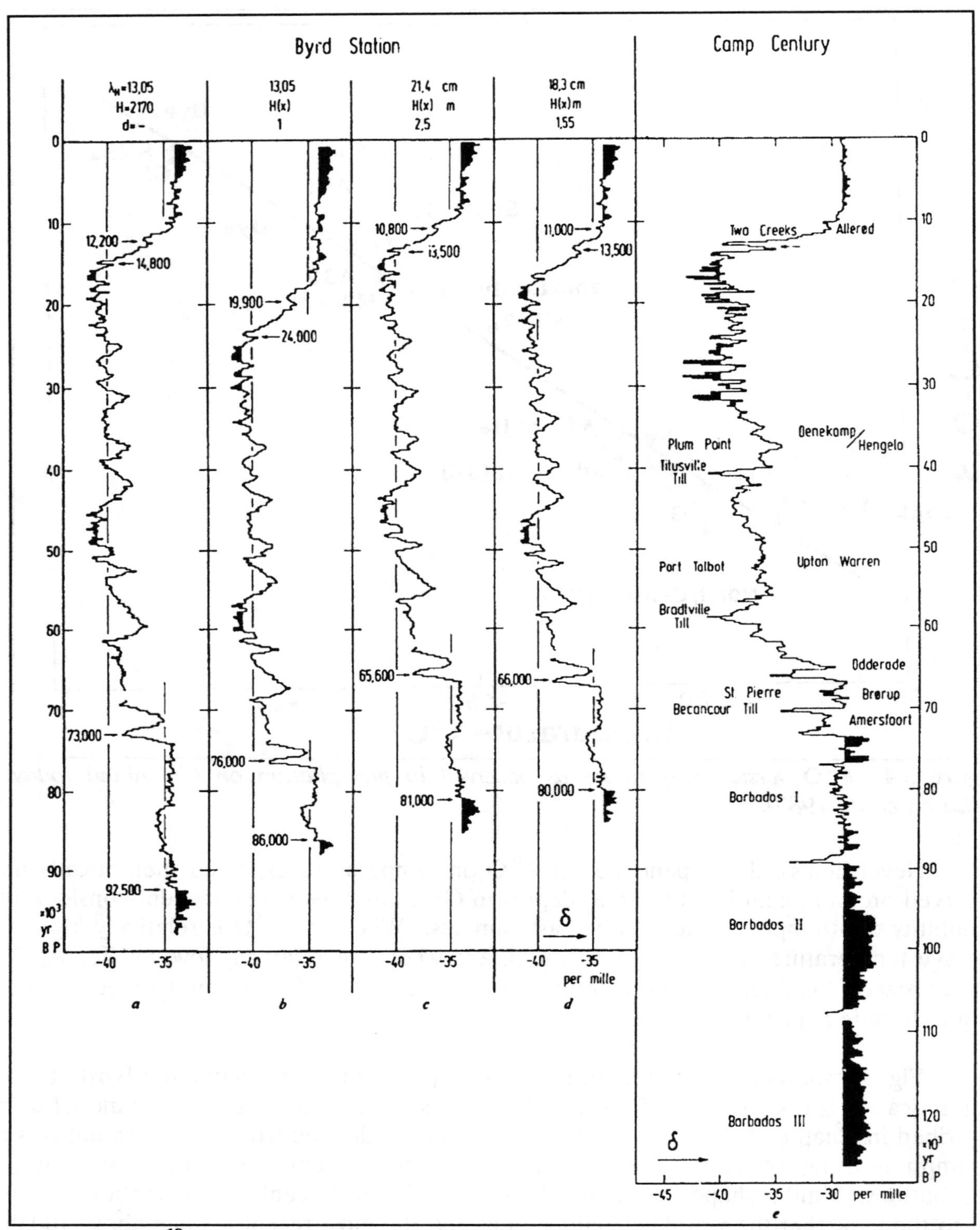


**Figure 3.5** $\delta^{18}O$ *versus long-age model time for Camp Century, Greenland and Byrd Station, Antarctica (Johnsen et al., 1972).*

B.P. Rather rapidly, the climate warmed, the glaciers receded, and the earth entered the Holocene epoch about 11,000 years B.P. Since then the climate has remained relatively warm in the current "interglacial" period.

This model has gained wide acceptance and has colored the interpretation of many other fields of study. However, unrecognized by many researchers are significant problems with this model and the data supporting it. Three of the more serious problems will be discussed in detail to illustrate this.

Dating Problems with the Old Ice in Greenland

Fig. 3.6 shows the $\delta^{18}O$ profiles from about 300 meters of the deepest parts of the ice cores through the ice sheets at Dye 3 in southeast Greenland and Camp Century in northwest Greenland. The ice deposited during the last glaciation is situated from 1786 meters to 2015 meters depth in the Dye 3 core and from 1157 meters to 1343 meters depth in the Camp Century core, as indicated by the generally more negative $\delta$s.

The numbered double arrows point to layers of estimated equal age in the two cores, to call attention to similarities in the records. Arrows 1 and 2 are highly questionable, because at 1950 meters depth the Dye 3 core contains a visible layer of solid particles, apparently from the bedrock, which suggests that the deepest 87 meters of the record may not represent a continuous time series. The reason has been suggested to be the hilly bedrock topography upstream from Dye 3 (Overgaard and Gundestrup, 1985), which complicates the flow of the deepest ice.

Dating of the layers indicated by Arrows 9 and 10 in Fig. 3.6 was accomplished by counting annual layers downward from the surface (Hammer et al., 1986), continuously through the last 5900 years. The dating prior to the Younger Dryas, however, is unsatisfactory, i.e., below Arrow 9. This is due to:

1) Seasonal $\delta^{18}O$ variations, which are a powerful tool for absolute dating of Holocene ice by annual layer identification, have been obliterated by diffusion in the older ice (Johnsen, 1977).

2) Seasonal acidity variations are suppressed in most of the Pleistocene ice in Greenland. This ice is alkaline, due to the high alkaline aerosol load that apparently neutralized the atmospheric acids, at least at high northern latitudes (Hammer et al., 1985).

3) Ice-flow modeling has so far not been able to provide a reliable time scale through the Pleistocene ice in the two existing deep Greenland ice cores. In contrast to the recent Vostok core, they were both drilled far from the main ice divide, and in areas where the Pleistocene ice is situated, only some 200 meters above bedrock.

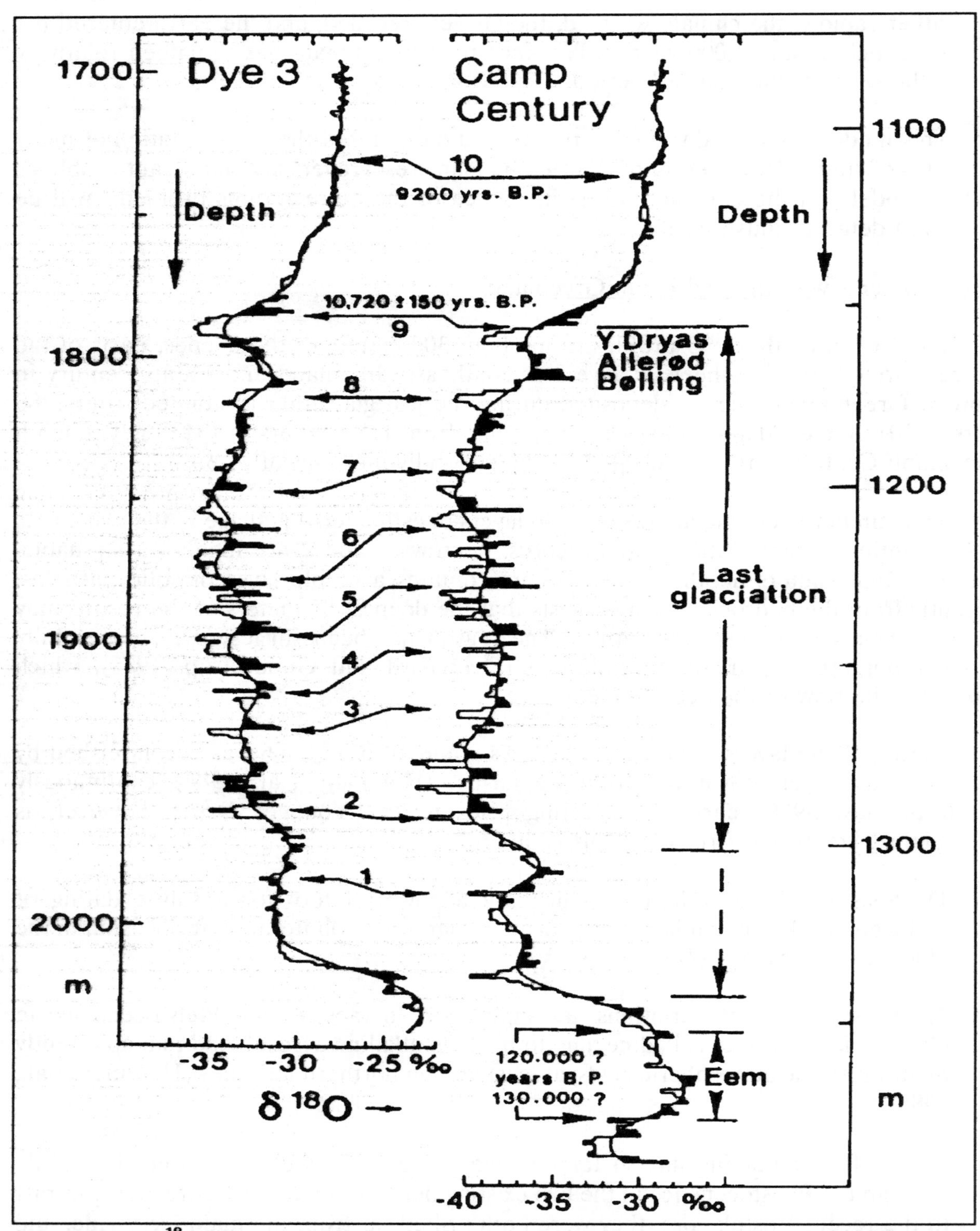


**Figure 3.6** *$\delta^{18}$O versus depth for the bottom of Dye 3 and Camp Century, Greenland cores (Dansgaard et al., 1982).*

4) Until recently, radiocarbon dating of glacier ice required more ice than was available in the deep ice cores. In the future, the new accelerator mass spectrometer technique may make radiocarbon dating possible.

Lack of Correspondence Between the Antarctic and Greenland Records

The Camp Century, Greenland, deep ice core is believed by some researchers to reveal seasonal variations in the isotopic composition of the ice back to about 8,300 years B.P. (Johnsen et al., 1972). This is not the case for the Byrd Station, Antarctica, deep ice core. But, both cores do show long-term perturbations in isotopic composition reflecting climatic changes from before the beginning of the last glaciation. The complexity of the glaciological regime at Byrd Station precludes an undisputed choice of a time scale. Pole-to-pole correlations of the paleoclimatic data are said to be speculative, except for the more pronounced features and general trends (Johnsen et al., 1972).

The $\delta^{18}O$ records are compared in Fig. 3.5. The short-term $\delta^{18}O$ oscillations during late glacial time are more pronounced in the Camp Century record than in the Byrd Station record, whereas the $\delta^{18}O$ curve for the post-glacial period at Byrd Station shows a more pronounced variability than does the Camp Century curve. A possible explanation for the stable character of the Camp Century curve in the post-glacial is the stabilizing effect of Baffin Bay close to Camp Century.

Another interesting difference between the two records is that the post-glacial climatic optimum is revealed at Camp Century, whereas the post-glacial Byrd Station record shows pronounced oscillations and a shift from -34‰ up to 4,000 B.P., to -33‰ after about 2,500 B.P. The reason for this is not clear, particularly since the post-glacial climatic optimum between 8,000 and 4,500 B.P. has been recognized in the Southern Hemisphere (Auer, 1960). The generally increasing tendency of the $\delta^{18}O$ curve was noticed also by Epstein et al. (1970), who suggested it was due to the deeper strata originating from higher altitudes (with lower temperatures of deposition). However, it easily can be shown that the Byrd core was formed at an altitude of less than 50 meters higher than the 2,000-year-old strata, corresponding to a temperature difference of less than 0.5°C. That is not enough to explain a difference of more than 1‰ in the $\delta^{18}O$. Thus, the assumption of steady state may not be valid. It seems more likely that the thickness of the ice sheet has diminished by a few hundred meters since the glaciation or some other process was occurring.

Apparently, because of the complicated glaciological regime existing at Byrd Station, interpretation of the $\delta^{18}O$ record in the Byrd core is not straightforward, and contains many pitfalls. Because of the uncertainties involved, it is not advisable to attempt to compare the detailed interpretation of Camp Century with the Byrd record, nor to estimate possible phase differences between climatic fluctuation within the Wisconsin glaciation revealed by the two records (Johnsen et al., 1972). Nevertheless, certain trends in the $\delta^{18}O$ records suggest a correlation with pronounced Northern Hemispheric climatic events, which has been used tentatively to adjust the time scale along the Byrd Station core.

## Sudden Warming After the Younger Dryas

Three different general circulation models indicate that at 18,000 B.P. the mass balance of the polar ice sheets was negative and that complete melting would occur over a period of a few thousand years (Manabe and Broccoli, 1985; Kurtzbach, 1987; Rind, 1987). With increased summer insolation during the termination of the "Ice Age," this mass imbalance would be increased. It has also been suggested that ice-sheet decay may have been driven by orbital forcing (Imbrie et al., 1984; Held, 1976; Held, 1979; Pollard, 1978; Pollard, et al., 1980; Weertmann, 1976) or at least modulated by orbital forcing (Sergin, 1980; Saltzman et al., 1981; Nicolis, 1984; Saltzman, 1985). Orbital forcing is the effect on cooling and heating of the atmosphere by small differences in earth-sun distance associated with orbital parameters.

Calculations suggest that $CO_2$-induced air temperature changes were large enough to cause disintegration of an extensive marine-based ice sheet on Eurasia (Lindstrom and MacAyeal, 1989). Initial ice-sheet disintegration is suggested to have led to "ungrounding" of the marine-based ice sheet which, in turn, resulted in rapid flow toward ablation areas. Surface warming supposedly enhanced the ablation, and ice-sheet disintegration was accomplished in about 4,000 years.

The calculated rate of change in climate at Arrow 9 (the Younger Dryas to the preboreal boundary) in Fig. 3.6 is very large and extremely well defined in both the Camp Century and Byrd Station cores. In the Dye 3 core, $\delta^{18}O$ shifted from -35.2‰ to -30.5‰ within a one-meter increment. At the same time, the annual layer thickness increased from approximately 2.1 cm to 3.4 cm (Hammer et al., 1986), indicating a transition period on the order of 40 years.

During this short-time interval, the environmental conditions changed drastically in the North American region. In Greenland, the mean-air temperature rose 7°C, as estimated from Eq. 3.2. The accumulation rate increased approximately 60%, to judge from the rapidly increasing annual layer thickness, and the dust content, acidity, and chemical composition of the deposited ice changed (Hammer et al., 1985; Herron and Langway, 1985). In the North Atlantic Ocean, the winter ice-cover boundary was pushed far northwards (Ruddiman and McIntyre, 1981) to the eastern part, from Biscay into the Norwegian Sea. Also in Europe, a rapid change of the flora is seen in all pollen diagrams.

The total $\delta^{18}O$ shift during the Pleistocene to Holocene transition amounts to about 7‰ in the Dye 3 core and about 11‰ in the Camp Century core. According to Eq. 3.2, this corresponds to a warming of about 10.5 and 16.4°C, respectively. The apparent stronger warming trend in the Camp Century area agrees with data from an Ellesmere Island ice core (Fisher et al., 1983) substantiating the interpretation that global climatic changes seem to be generally more pronounced in the higher latitudes.

Is simply melting of the ice sufficient to explain the observed rate of climate change during the deglaciation? Broecker and Denton (1989) argue that much of the planet had warmed considerably by about 12,000 B.P., when the Laurentide Ice Sheet was still of significant size. Thus, some sort of abrupt transition may have been responsible for the warming (Flohn, 1979, 1986; Broecker et al., 1985). Broecker and Denton (1989) suggest that changes in the coupled ocean-atmosphere circulation in the North Atlantic were responsible for the warming. However, changes in ocean-atmosphere heat transport generally do not increase planetary temperatures, they only alter the distribution.

For example, Manabe and Stouffer (1988) demonstrate that when the North Atlantic is in an interglacial mode (warm North Atlantic and active North Atlantic Deep Water [NADW] formation), southern hemisphere temperatures are lower than when the circulation is in a "glacial" mode. This response reflects the fact that an interglacial-mode circulation in the North Atlantic is exporting cold NADW across the equator, and importing heat via warm Southern Hemisphere surface waters. During the glacial mode, export of warm waters from the Southern Hemisphere decreases; temperatures south of the equator rise accordingly.

There are at least two conditions which allow globally averaged temperature changes with altered ocean-atmosphere circulation. One involves changes in snow and ice cover, due to enhanced heat transport into high latitudes, and the change in albedo will change the planetary radiation balance. For example, onset of an interglacial mode North Atlantic circulation should cause a retreat of North Atlantic sea ice and a significant local increase in temperatures (Rind et al., 1986). However, the effect of North Atlantic changes on globally averaged temperatures is small -- 0.3°C for the energy-balance model discussed in Hyde et al. (1989).

Changes in the ocean-atmosphere system can also affect global temperatures through a $CO_2$ feedback. For example, Boyle (1988 a,b) discusses how changes in the thermohaline circulation could affect the vertical distribution of $CO_2$ in the ocean. However, this model requires a several-thousand-year-$CO_2$ lag in response to deep-circulation changes. $CO_2$ change, itself, also can cause global warmth. At present, the timing of $CO_2$ change does not support this scenario, but there is just enough uncertainty in the $CO_2$ measurements that we cannot eliminate this possibility with confidence.

There also may have been changes in dust cover (Petit et al., 1981, 1990; Hammer et al., 1985) and clouds (Charlson et al., 1987; Bates et al., 1987; Schwartz, 1988) over the past 20,000 years. Volcanism has been proposed (Flohn, 1979; Bryson, 1989), but it is doubted that the effect would be significant. It is not clear whether any of the above mechanisms can actually explain the magnitude of the warming at 13,000 years B.P. (Crowley and North, 1991).

What, then, caused the atmosphere to warm? The explanation for this warmth is an important unsolved question in paleoclimatology.

## CHAPTER 4

## BIBLICAL BOUNDARY CONDITIONS

The Bible does not speak directly about an "ice age" or glaciers. Nowhere do the Scriptures describe the vast sheets of ice which are currently in polar regions, nor do they discuss effects of glaciers which once covered even wider expanses of northern latitudes and mountain tops (Fig. 4.1). Yet, indirect references do occur in Scripture which may illustrate some familiarity with, and exposure to, colder, wetter climates. For example:

**Figure 4.1** ***Vast sheets of snow and ice cover northern latitudes and mountains today (Sella, 1888).***

> "Hast thou entered into the treasures of the snow? or hast thou seen the treasures of the hail" (Job 38:22)?

> "Out of whose womb came the ice? and the hoary frost of heaven, who hath gendered it" (Job 38:29)?

> "He giveth snow like wool: he scattereth the hoarfrost like ashes. He casteth forth his ice like morsels: who can stand before His cold" (Psalm 147: 16,17)?

Scripture also describes a generally wetter, more suitable climate for agriculture than that which is prevalent today in the Middle East for an indefinite period after the Flood. For example:

> "And Lot lifted up his eyes, and beheld all the plain of Jordan, that it was well watered every where, before the LORD destroyed Sodom and Gomorrah, even as the garden of the LORD, like the land of Egypt, as thou comest unto Zoar" (Genesis 13:10.)

"And the LORD said, I have surely seen the affliction of my people which are in Egypt, and have heard their cry by reason of their taskmasters; for I know their sorrows; And I am come down to deliver them out of the hand of the Egyptians, and to bring them up out of that land unto a good land and a large, unto a land flowing with milk and honey" (Exodus 3:7,8.)

Land-use studies throughout the Mediterranean, North Africa, and the Mideast show the prevalence of crops and forests which were suited to cooler, wetter climates in the period before 1000 B.C. Agriculture was common throughout portions of North Africa, which are deserts today. Satellite imagery of the Sahara shows river channels with complete tributary systems buried beneath the sand providing evidence of greater rainfall in the past (Fig. 4.2). The climate in the past, evident from these studies, would have been consistent with that expected just south of a glacial ice sheet in Europe and western Asia.

**Figure 4.2** ***River channels beneath the sands of the Sahara desert revealed by satellite imagery (NASA).***

The standard long-age model of earth history would agree with the general scenario of a cooler, wetter climate to the south of a mid-latitude glacier; however, the timing would be considerably different. A literal Biblical chronology of earth history would require the "Ice Age" to follow the great Flood described in Genesis 6-9, because the Flood produced the sedimentary-rock strata evident all over the earth, and the "Ice Age" evidence lies on top of these strata. A Biblical chronology like that of Ussher (1786) would place the "Ice

Age" between 1000 and 3000 years B.C. Other strict Biblical chronologies might move the "Ice Age" back in time by a few thousand years more, but none would project the "Ice Age" back to 18,000 B.P. A literal interpretation of the Bible could not in any way accommodate "Ice Ages" extending 160,000 years in the past (Jouzel et al., 1987) or older "Ice Ages" millions of years ago (Crowley and North, 1991).

The timing of a Biblical "Ice Age" then, hinges on the historicity of the great Flood. According to Scripture, the great Deluge in the days of Noah was a worldwide catastrophe in which "... the world that then was, being overflowed with water, perished" II Peter 3:6. That the Bible teaches a universal flood rather than a local or a regional flood is evident for many reasons, among which are the following, according to Morris (1984):

1) The flood waters covered all the high mountains (Gen. 7:19-20) and continued to cover them completely for about nine months (Genesis 8:5). These facts can answer hydraulically to a worldwide flood and to nothing else.

2) Expressions of universality in the account (Genesis 6-9) are not scattered and incidental (as is the case elsewhere in Scripture when apparently universal terms are used in a limited sense), but are repeated and emphasized again and again, constituting the very essence of the narrative. There are at least thirty times in which this universality ("all flesh," "every living thing," "all the high hills under the whole heaven," etc.) is mentioned in these chapters.

3) The worldwide character of the Flood is also assumed in later parts of Scripture. See especially the testimony of the psalmist (Psalm 104:7), of Peter (I Peter 3:20; II Peter 2:5; 3:5-6), and of the Lord Jesus Christ (Matthew 24:37-39).

4) The primary purpose of the Flood was to destroy all mankind. This is seen not only in the numerous statements in Genesis to that effect but also in those of Peter (II Peter 2:5) and of Christ (Luke 17:26-27). This could never have been accomplished by anything less than a global catastrophe. The wide distribution of early man is indicated by anthropological studies, but of even greater significance is the Biblical testimony concerning the extreme longevity and productivity of the antediluvians, who had been filling the earth for hundreds of years (Genesis 1:28; 6:1,11).

5) The tremendous size of the ark (which, according to the most conservative calculations, had a volumetric capacity equivalent to that of over five hundred standard railroad stock cars) is an eloquent witness that far more than a regional fauna was to be preserved therein. Its purpose was "to keep seed alive upon the face of all the earth" (Genesis 7:3), quite a pointless provision if the Deluge was local.

6) There would obviously have been no need for an ark at all if the Flood were anything other than universal. Noah and his family could far more easily have migrated to some distant land during the 120 years it took to build the ark. Similarly, the birds and animals of the region could much more simply have been preserved by a process of migration. The Flood narrative is thus made entirely ridiculous by the local-flood hypothesis.

7) God's thrice-repeated promise (Genesis 8:21; 9:11,15) never again to "smite every thing living" by a flood clearly applies only to a universal catastrophe. If the promise referred only to a local flood, it has been repeatedly broken every time there has been a destructive flood anywhere in the world. The local flood notion therefore not only charges Scripture with error, but maintains that God does not keep His promises!

The seven reasons listed above are only a few out of many. In his commentary on Genesis, Morris (1976) has given one hundred reasons why the Flood must be regarded as universal.

If one accepts the historicity of the great Flood and its devastation of the earth in the recent past, then how does one understand the ice-core data to fit within a Biblical framework? The specifics of this reinterpretation will be dealt with in Chapters 5 and 6 of this report.

The general features are discussed by Oard (1990) and are as follows:

1) At the end of the great Flood, the oceans were uniformly warmer than today, from top to bottom and from equator to pole.

2) Radiation deficits at the poles and over the continents caused rapid cooling.

3) Evaporation of vast quantities of water from the oceans fed the growth of ice sheets at the poles and on mountain tops.

4) The growth of polar ice sheets increased the earth's albedo which caused even greater cooling and further progression of glaciers to midlatitudes on the continents and nearly as far equatorward over the oceans (Fig. 4.4).

5) When the oceans had cooled to near equilibrium, the evaporation slowed and glaciation slowed, stopped, and then reversed.

6) The formation of polar glaciers began when sufficient cooling of the polar regions had occurred such that snow could accumulate (probably before 2000 years B.C.)

7) The major growth and retreat of the glaciers probably occurred before 1000 years B.C.

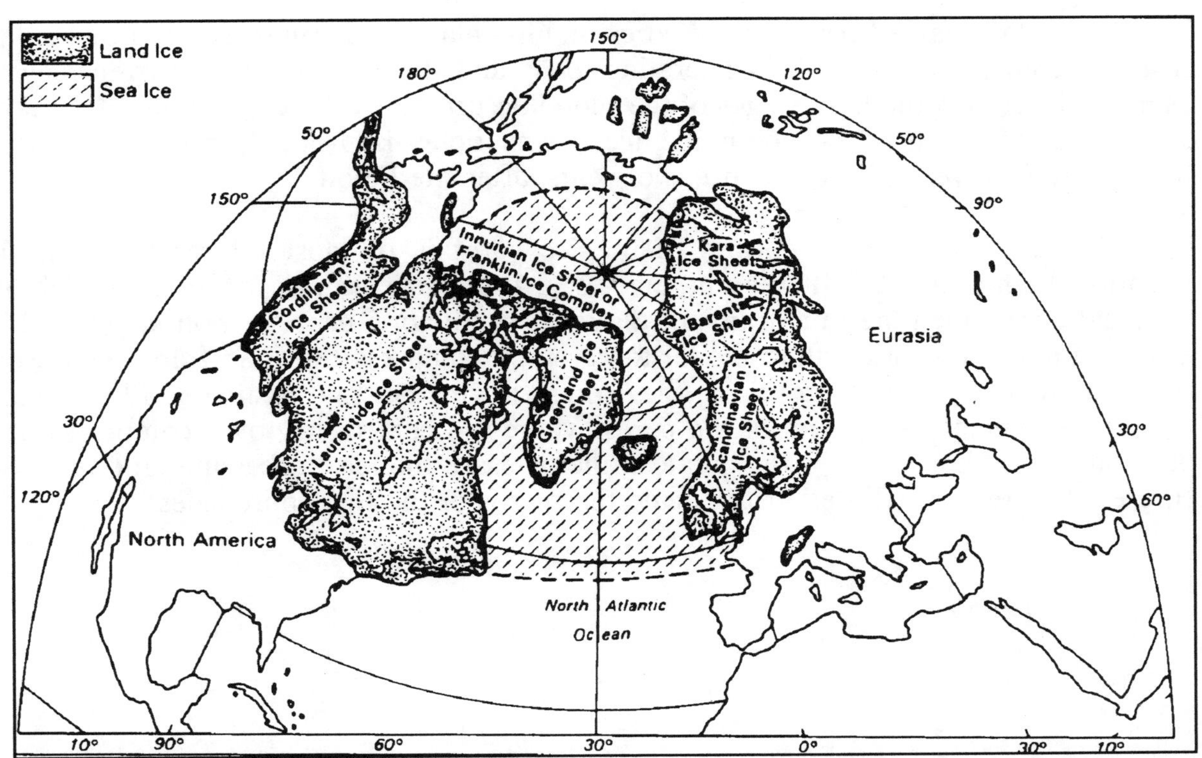


**Figure 4.3** ***The maximum extent of the northern hemisphere ice sheets during the "Ice Age" (Crowley and North, 1991).***

The approach we will use in the reinterpretation is to take the data that have been obtained from ice-core drillings and reinterpret them in terms of a Biblical framework of earth history. Some may object that this is mixing religion and science; however, the approach is no different, in fact, than that of the conventional long-age model. The long-age model assumes that there was no supernatural agent active in creating the world in the recent past or in bringing judgement to this world by a worldwide Flood. Consequently, billions of years are needed in an attempt to explain its origin and processes. This world view is then imposed upon the data to find an interpretation.

We will assume a different framework. The recent-creation model, which I will use, assumes God created the world in a supernatural creative event some 6,000 years ago, and judged his creation through a worldwide catastrophic Flood some 4,500 or so years ago. The assumption that the Flood occurred 4,500 years ago is derived from the Ussher chronology using the Textus Receptus. Some would choose a longer chronology based on the Septuagint and relaxation of some time constraints. However, this author prefers this date, at least to start the study. Between God's supernatural intervention in the affairs of the world, He normally allows the physical processes to operate according to the laws of science. We wish to determine whether the ice core data can be reasonably explained within this conceptual framework.

The data obtained from the ice cores on Greenland and Antarctica can be studied and interpreted according to laws operating today and since the Flood. It even may be possible to infer how the later stages of the Flood occurred, if we are fortunate. However, most of the information locked in the ice at the poles is probably representative of conditions tens of years, if not hundreds of years, after the Flood.

The data at the very bottom of the ice cores is of most interest to both the conventional and the recent-creation models. The conventional long-age model has dramatically expanded the time frame of the ice accumulation near the bottom. It will be necessary for the recent-creation model to carefully compress the time frame of the ice accumulation near the bottom of the cores to match my assumed Flood date. Unfortunately, near the bottom of the cores, where the controversy over compression or expansion of the time frame is the greatest, the data are the least accessible and the least accurate. The reader will be left to decide the merits of the two approaches.

# CHAPTER 5

## NUMERICAL MODELING

In principle, it is possible to use the seasonal variation of $\delta^{18}O$ measured from small samples of ice cores and count the summer maxima and winter minima downward from the surface, like tree rings, to obtain a chronology. However, not only does this procedure require a large number of measurements, it also does not extend deeply into the ice sheet, because molecular diffusion gradually obliterates the short-term oscillations that remain after firnification, particularly in Antarctica. Johnsen et al. (1972) have stated:

> ... in principle dating of the Camp Century ice core by counting annual layers is possible to about 1,060 m depth, corresponding to 8,300 yr BP according to the time scale which we shall adopt. It may be necessary, however, to apply a depth dependent correction to account for "lost" annual oscillations. Even during firnification seasonal $\delta$-oscillations in years with unusually low accumulation may disappear due to mass exchange. Unfortunately, the physical condition (broken or missing pieces) of the Camp Century ice core precludes continuous measurement of seasonal isotope variations for the purpose of dating from the surface downward.
>
> The physical condition of the Byrd Station ice core is considerably better. Nevertheless ... seasonal cycles are difficult to interpret in such low accumulation areas.

It is true that annual layers can be counted downward in Greenland through several thousand layers. It is also true that counting of layers can be accomplished "in principle" even deeper. However, counting "in principle" is an admission that literal counting of annual layers has not actually been done. The reason given is that sections of the ice core from Greenland are missing or broken, or low accumulation in some years has caused some layers to disappear.

It is also assumed by Johnsen et al. (1972) that the layers they have counted are "annual" layers. This is valid near the top of the Greenland ice sheet, but probably has little merit below several thousand layers. The time scale they apply to the layers is dependent upon model calculations. It is not derived from the counting of layers but from a flow model, which has many questionable assumptions. No estimate is given for how deeply into the Antarctic ice sheet annual layers may be counted, but it is inferred that the number is much less than Greenland because of the much-lower accumulation rate.

It is the contention of this author that assurances that annual ice layers may be counted to as far back as 8,300 B.P. are unfounded. I believe several thousand layers are in evidence on Greenland, many of which could have accumulated in a relatively short period of time. The number of layers on Antarctica are fewer because of the low accumulation rate, and probably bear little relation to age.

I will attempt, in this chapter, to develop a model which can explain the formation of several thousand layers of ice on Greenland within about 4,500 years. The model will be constrained by as many known boundary conditions as possible, and refined, as more detailed ice-core data become available.

A commonly used method for counting layers is to calculate the age-depth relationships of the ice core by developing a physical model that incorporates a generally accepted flow theory (as suggested by the thin curves in Fig. 5.1) and reasonable assumptions concerning the parameters that influence it. Dansgaard et al. (1969) and Dansgaard et al. (1971) have applied this technique to the Camp Century, Greenland core, and Lorius et al. (1979) to the Dome C, Antarctic core.

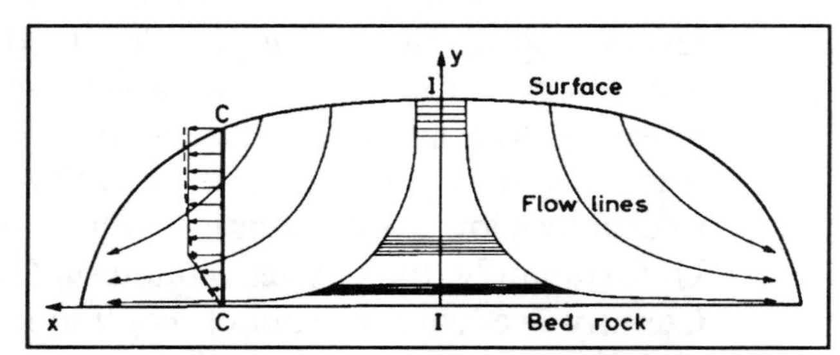

**Figure 5.1** ***Flow model of ice flowing outward from an ice divide (Dansgaard, et al., 1971).***

Fig. 5.1 shows a vertical section of an ice sheet resting on bedrock. The ice divide (a topographic feature from which ice diverges) is denoted by I-I. The ice deposited on the surface at location I is buried by succeeding snowfalls, and sinks into the ice sheet. At the same time, the layers accumulated annually become thinner by plastic deformation, as the ice flows horizontally outward from the ice divide. The core from Camp Century is shown at C-C. It contains ice formed upstream from Camp Century under similar environmental conditions. The horizontal, upper-surface velocity of the ice at Camp Century is 3.3 meters per year (Mock, 1968), and, therefore, even a 15,000-year-old deep section of the ice core would originate less than 50 kilometers further inland.

We will consider several flow models and assumptions in this chapter. These models are quite simplistic, and are recognized to be only a first approximation to an ice-core chronology (Dansgaard et al., 1971). Near the end of this treatment, we will present several completely unique assumptions which are suggested by the ice-age model of Oard (1990) and lead to a preliminary recent-creation chronology. The alternative assumptions involve a greater accumulation rate immediately after the Flood and a finite-layer thickness near the bottom of the core, rather than zero-thickness layers, which imply an infinite amount of time since the origin of the ice sheet.

We first consider the classical Nye flow model (Nye, 1951; 1957; 1959), which assumes that the horizontal velocity component of the ice, $V_x$, is uniform along the core. We assume an infinite sheet of ice of uniform thickness of H meters, which accumulates snow everywhere on its upper surface at a rate of $\lambda_H/\tau$ meters/year (Fig. 5.2). Thinning of the ice sheet is restricted to the y direction, and horizontal flow to the x direction only. This model implies sliding on the bottom.

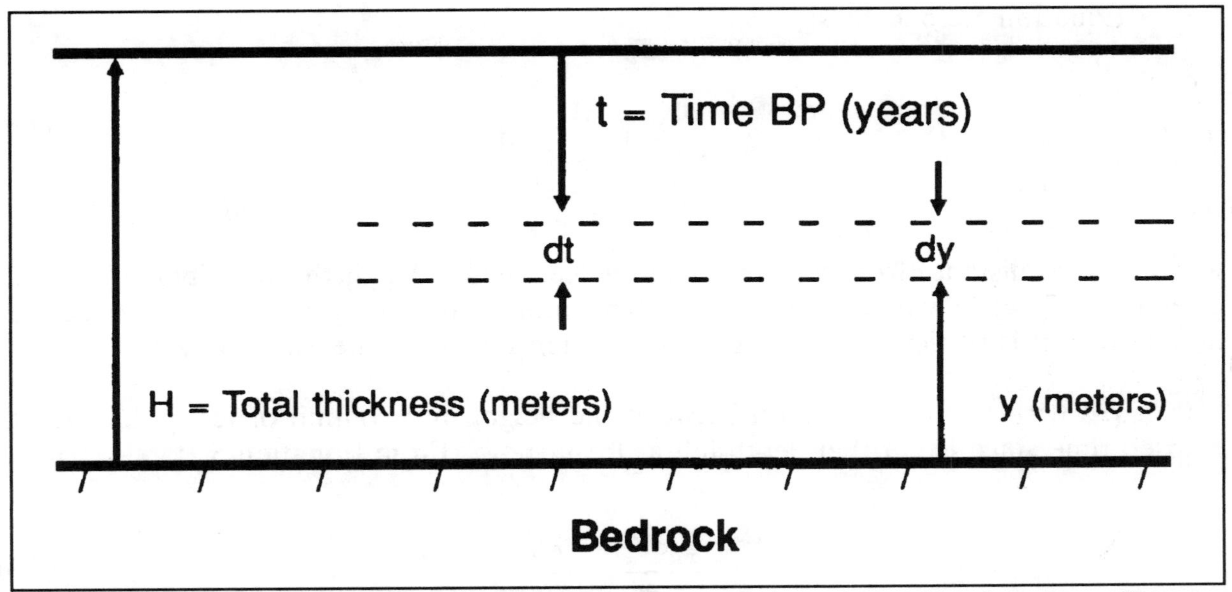


**Figure 5.2** *Schematic of time and height variables of a layer in an ice sheet at a distance, x, from the ice divide.*

For an ice sheet in mass balance (the accumulation rate from precipitation equals the ablation rate by compression and spreading) the continuity equation is:

$$\frac{\lambda_H}{\tau} x = V_x H \qquad (5.1)$$

where $\tau$ is the accumulation period in years (typically one year), $\lambda_H$ is the accumulation over the accumulation period in meters of ice, x is the horizontal distance from the ice divide along the flow direction, $V_x$ is the velocity in the x direction, and H is the thickness of the ice sheet in meters.

If the ice is assumed to be incompressible, then the divergence of the velocity is zero, or:

$$\nabla \cdot \mathbf{V} = 0 \qquad (5.2)$$

where $\mathbf{V} = \mathbf{i}V_x + \mathbf{j}V_y$, the total velocity vector.

Equation 5.2 becomes:

$$\frac{\partial V_x}{\partial x} + \frac{\partial V_y}{\partial y} = 0 \tag{5.3}$$

where y is the distance from the bottom of the ice sheet and $V_y$ is the velocity in the upward direction. Since it will be assumed that no motion or divergence occurs in the third direction, z, it is sufficient to consider the problems in two dimensions only.

We wish to find a relation between the height in a column of ice, y, and $\Delta t$, the elapsed time since ice at that depth fell as fresh snow. From Equation 5.1:

$$\frac{\partial V_x}{\partial x} = \frac{\lambda_H}{H\tau} \tag{5.4}$$

Combining Equation 5.3 and Equation 5.4:

$$\frac{\partial V_x}{\partial x} = -\frac{\partial V_y}{\partial y} = \frac{\lambda_H}{H\tau} \tag{5.5}$$

Solving for $V_y$:

$$\int_0^{V_y} dV_y = -\frac{\lambda_H}{H\tau}\int_0^y dy \tag{5.6}$$

or:

$$V_y = -\frac{\lambda_H}{H\tau} y \tag{5.7}$$

The time in the past when a given layer was laid down can then, theoretically, be calculated from the following:

$$V_y = \frac{dy}{dt} \tag{5.8}$$

or:

$$dt = \frac{dy}{V_y} \tag{5.9}$$

Integrating downward from the surface in the y direction corresponds to an integration backward in time. At the surface
y = H and t = 0, so:

$$\int_0^{\Delta t} dt = \int_H^y \frac{dy}{V_y} \tag{5.10}$$

or, from Equation 5.7:

$$\Delta t = -\frac{H\tau}{\lambda_H}\int_H^y \frac{dy}{y} = \frac{H\tau}{\lambda_H}\ln\frac{H}{y} \tag{5.11}$$

This equation seems to fit the upper layers of the ice sheet at Camp Century fairly well. The parameters necessary are $\lambda_H$, the average annual accumulation at the surface, and H, the total thickness of the ice sheet. The mean annual accumulation at Camp Century for the past 100 years is $\lambda_H = 0.35 \pm 0.04$ meters of ice (Crozaz and Langway, 1966). H is 1390 meters at Camp Century, Greenland.

Fig. 5.3 shows a graph of Equation 5.11 with $\lambda_H = .35$ meters, H = 1390, and $\tau$ = 1 year. Note that t approaches infinity, as y approaches 0. However, the equation only predicts an age of about 20,000 years for the layer 10 meters above bedrock. This "young" age does not fit well with the old-earth model, which expects an age in excess of 100,000 years at this depth (Fig. 3.7). It is necessary for long-age modelers to make further adjustments, if the presumed older ages of the ice at the bottom of the ice sheet are to be fit into the model. On the other hand, the equation predicts ages which are too old for a Flood date of 4,500 B.P. Other adjustments will need to be made for my model.

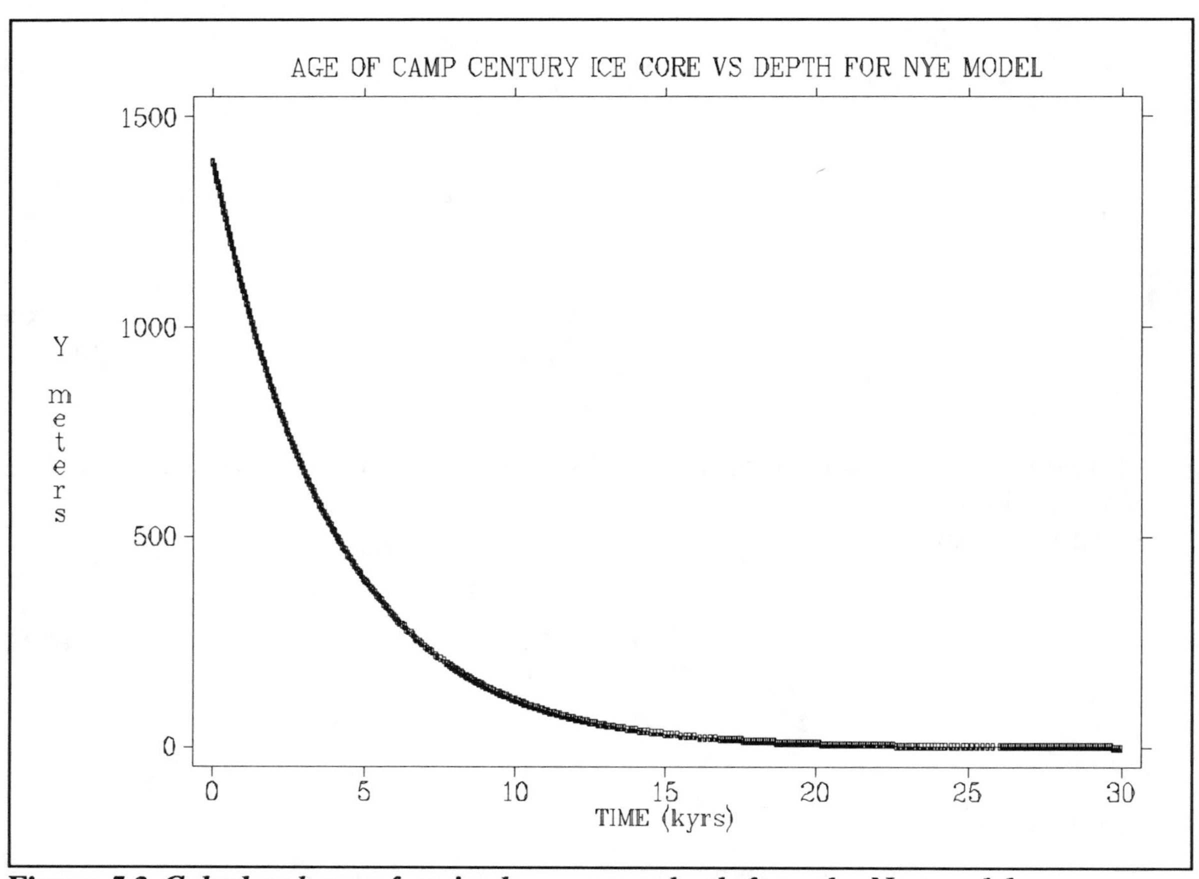


**Figure 5.3** ***Calculated age of an ice layer versus depth from the Nye model.***

This equation fits neither a presumed old-earth model nor my recent-creation model. It should be remembered that such equations do not require the physical processes to have occurred in a particular way, but are rather the result of the initial assumptions about the physical processes.

The Nye model assumes that the ice sheet slides freely along the bottom. However, the present temperature at the bedrock interface is -13°C (Hanson and Langway, 1966). The ice is therefore frozen to the bottom, and $V_x$ must be zero for $y = 0$, invalidating Nye's model at great depths.

Recognizing that Nye's model was inadequate for Camp Century, Dansgaard et al. (1971) used stress-and-strain relations to develop a more realistic horizontal velocity profile in a second model (Weertman, 1968). The model calculated the horizontal velocity component, $V_x$, shown as a dashed line at C-C in Fig. 5.1, by integrating Glen's law,

$$\dot{\epsilon} = k\sigma^n \; ; \qquad V_x = \int_0^y k\sigma^n dy \tag{5.12}$$

where $\dot{\epsilon}$ and $\sigma$ are the shear strain rate and the shear stress, respectively, and k and n are experimentally determined constants that depend on the temperature profile along the Camp Century core. Applying the approximation, shown by the solid curve along C-C in Fig. 5.1 ($V_x$ uniform down to y = h = 400 meters), and following a similar procedure as with the Nye model, the age-versus-depth relationship becomes:

$$\Delta t = \frac{(2H-h)\tau}{2\lambda_H} \ln \frac{2H-h}{2y-h} \; ; \qquad h \le y \le H \tag{5.13}$$

$$\Delta t = t_h + \frac{(2H-h)\tau}{2\lambda_H}\left(\frac{h}{y} - 1\right) \; ; \qquad 0 < y \le h \tag{5.14}$$

Equations 5.13 and 5.14 involve $\lambda_H$, the accumulation at the surface of the ice sheet; h, the height above the bedrock at which the horizontal velocity component becomes uniform with height; and H, the total thickness of the ice sheet. Dansgaard et al. (1971) used H = 1370 meters in these equations instead of the actual 1390 meter ice thickness at Camp Century to account for the lower densities in the upper firn layers. They also used $\lambda_H$ = 0.35 meters; the mean for the last 100 years. One century is only a small fraction of the time range of interest, and Dansgaard et al. (1971) recognized that it was not necessarily representative of the accumulation over the entire depth. In fact, they state, "... $\lambda_H$ is a function of t, and it is impossible to find the relationship between these two parameters if only for the reason that a given annual layer has undergone plastic thinning, which depends upon the temperature it has been exposed to since deposition." Superimposed upon the temporal variations of $\lambda_H$, there is also a time-dependent geographical variation. Consequently, the time scale of Equations 5.13 and 5.14 is only a first approximation to the real chronology. In fact, Dansgaard et al. (1971) have attempted to refine their efforts at calculating a chronology by breaking the Camp Century ice core into three segments which exhibit physical cohesiveness, and applying Equations 5.13 and 5.14 sequentially.

Fig. 5.4 shows the measured values of $\delta^{18}O$ versus depth for Camp Century, Greenland. Note the relatively uniform $\delta^{18}O$ values from the surface to approximately 1000 meters depth. Below 1000 meters, the values decrease suddenly and then slowly increase again to a depth of 1370 meters. The uniform region is typically identified as the Holocene epoch. The maximum extent of the "last Ice Age" calculated to have occurred at about 18,000 B.P. by long-age modelers, is typically identified with the "valley" at the bottom of the record.

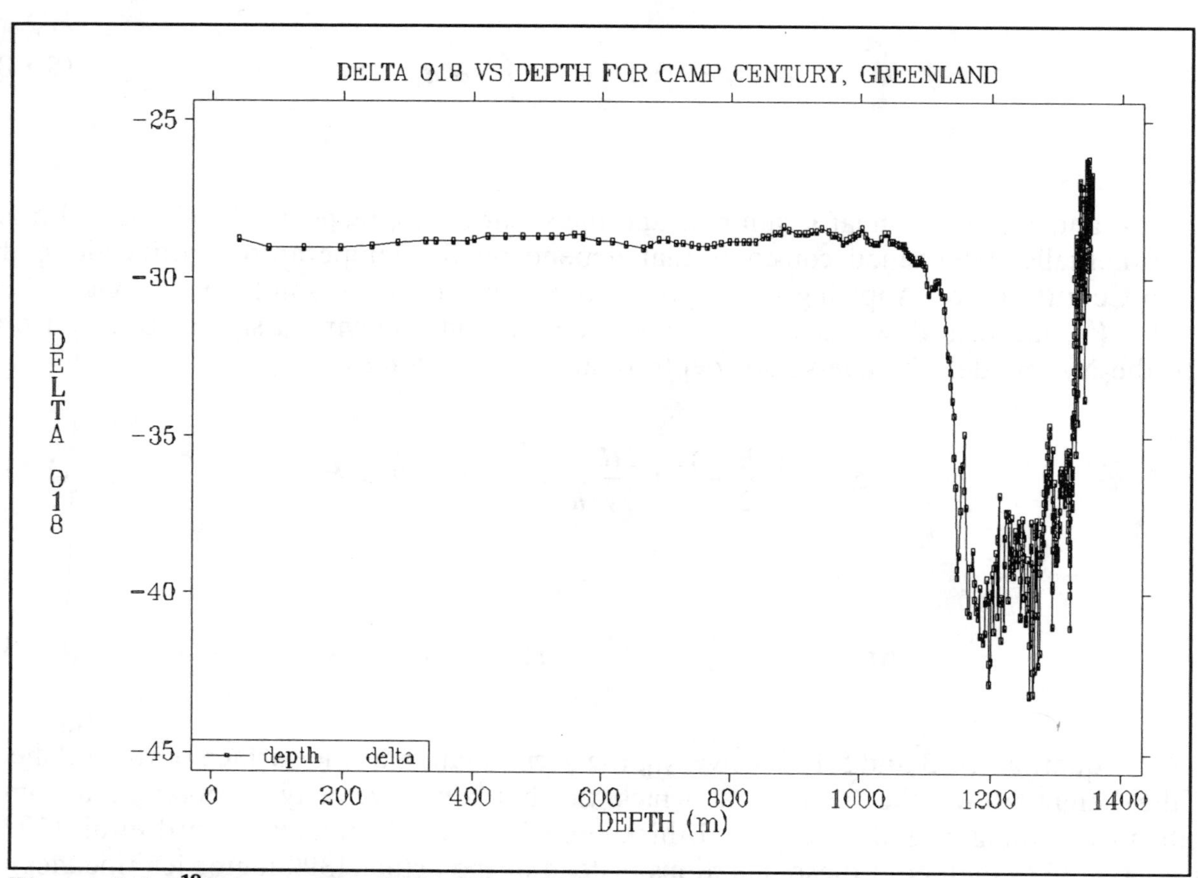


**Figure 5.4 $\delta^{18}O$ *versus depth for Camp Century, Greenland.***

Fig. 5.5 shows the measured values of $\delta^{18}O$ versus the calculated values of time from Equations 5.13 and 5.14. Note how the data between 1000 and 1370 meters have been expanded dramatically in this process. In fact, the data near the bottom are stretched the most, as would be expected from the inverse y relationship in Equation 5.14. Time approaches infinity, as y approaches 0. The oldest ice near the bottom of the Camp Century core is estimated by Johnsen et al. (1972) to be over 120,000 years.

In both of the long-age models which we have discussed above, it was assumed that new snow has been accumulating on the top of the ice sheet, at an average rate of $\lambda_H/\tau$, without interruption or significant perturbation for an infinite amount of time in the past. It is this uniformitarian assumption which gives rise to the very great ages for the bottom ice (infinite age at the very bottom) which these models yield. This assumption of uninterrupted conditions similar to those observed at present is not appropriate for a Biblical, global-flood model of the past. In particular, we would expect the oldest layers of ice to post-date the Flood (i.e. have a finite age), and climatological considerations suggest that the annual accumulation of snow would have been much greater than the presently observed value, $\lambda_H$, in the early years following the Flood. To illustrate what can happen

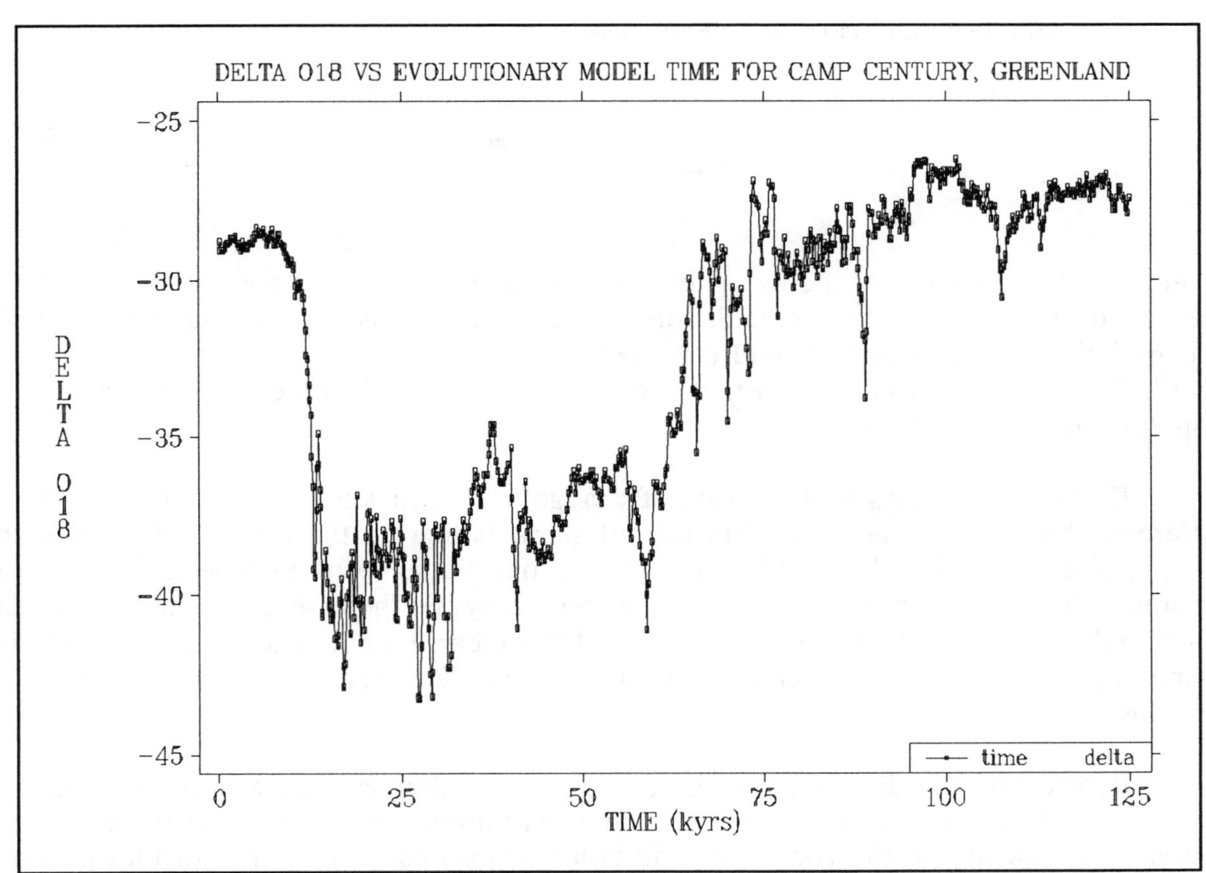


**Figure 5.5 $\delta^{18}$O *versus long-age model time.***

when assumptions which are more in line with a Flood model are used, consider the following simple model:

Assume that a sheet of ice of thickness, H, accumulates snow on its upper surface at a rate of $\lambda/\tau$ meters/year, where $\lambda$ is the accumulation in meters over a time period $\tau$ in years. In this case we will not assume that the ice sheet is in mass balance, but, rather, that it grows rapidly following the Flood, and later slowly approaches the equilibrium condition observed today. This means that H is a function of time, rather than being constant as the uniformitarian model requires. In fact, H will be assumed to be 0 at t = 0, the end of the Flood. A more complex model could be considered in the future, in which H is equal to 0 for some period after the Flood, until the temperature is cold enough for snow to begin to accumulate. The thickness of the ice sheet is then a function of the accumulation rate and the rate of thinning. The conventional long-age model developed a flow regime based on a two-dimensional assumption of incompressibility (Equation 5.2). However, in this model, I will use a linear-thinning function which is calibrated by the observed compression in the upper 4000 layers. In other words, the compression of an ice layer will be proportional to the thickness of the ice sheet.

This simple model can then be expressed as:

$$\frac{dH}{dt} = \lambda/\tau - \delta H \tag{5.15}$$

where H is the thickness of the ice sheet in meters as a function of time, t is the time since the Flood in years, $\tau$ is the accumulation period in years, $\lambda$ is the accumulation over the accumulation period in meters, and $\delta$ is the thinning ratio in year$^{-1}$. The thinning ratio is a constant and will be determined by the boundary conditions imposed on Equation 5.15.

Equation 5.15 says that the rate of change in the thickness of the ice sheet is the difference between the accumulation rate of snow, falling on the upper surface and the compression of the ice sheet which is linearly proportional to its thickness. This model assumes a linear thinning function which may not always be the case, particularly when the stress and strain are outside the elastic limits. Non-linear thinning may occur when the ice is melting, during massive surging, or when the underlying terrain constrains horizontal motions.

Before we can solve Equation 5.15, we need to assume a functional form for $\lambda$. We have reason to believe, from our Flood model, that immediately following the Flood the oceans were warm and the continents and polar regions cold, compared to that of today (Oard, 1991). If this was the case, the precipitation rate likely would have been much greater than that of today, and would have decreased with time. We will assume an exponentially decreasing accumulation function, which approaches today's rate in the limit. For this initial model, we will further assume that the accumulation rate at the end of the Flood was ten times that of today.

The functional form of $\lambda$ described in the preceding paragraph is:

$$\lambda = \lambda_H(9e^{\frac{-t}{\psi}} + 1) \tag{5.16}$$

where $\lambda_H$ is the accumulation over a period of interest observed today, t is the time since the Flood, and $\psi$ is the e-folding time of the decrease in accumulation since the Flood. The e-folding time will be determined by the shape of the distribution of layers to be explored shortly. Note that when $t = 0$ in Equation 5.16 $\lambda = 10\ \lambda_H$ and when $t = \infty$ $\lambda = \lambda_H$.

Combining Eqs. 5.15 and 5.16 and arranging into a standard form for solution of a linear, time-dependent differential equation gives:

$$\frac{dH}{dt} + \delta H = \frac{\lambda_H}{\tau}(9e^{\frac{-t}{\psi}} + 1) \tag{5.17}$$

The solution to this equation is:

$$H = \frac{\lambda_H}{\tau\delta}(1 - e^{-\delta t}) + \frac{9\lambda_H}{\tau(\delta - \frac{1}{\psi})}(e^{\frac{-t}{\psi}} - e^{-\delta t}) \tag{5.18}$$

Note that Equation 5.18 satisfies the boundary condition that H = 0 when t = 0. By applying another boundary condition, $\delta$ can be determined. Assume that H = 1370 meters when t = ∞. Under this condition, Equation 5.18 reduces to:

$$H\ (t = \infty) = \frac{\lambda_H}{\tau\delta} = 1370\ m \tag{5.19}$$

or:

$$\delta = \frac{\lambda_H}{(1370\ m)(\tau)} = 2.55 \times 10^{-4}\ year^{-1} \tag{5.20}$$

Fig. 5.6 shows the thickness of the Camp Century, Greenland ice sheet, H, plotted as a function of time since the Flood for a certain selection of parameters. In this case, $\lambda_H$ = .35 m, $\tau$ = 1 year, $\delta$ = 2.55 × $10^{-4}$ $year^{-1}$, $\psi$ = 400 years, and the time since the Flood t = 4,500 years. Note that H starts at 0, increases rapidly, and assymtotically approaches today's thickness of 1370 meters. For smaller values of $\psi$, the assymtotic approach to today's value is slower.

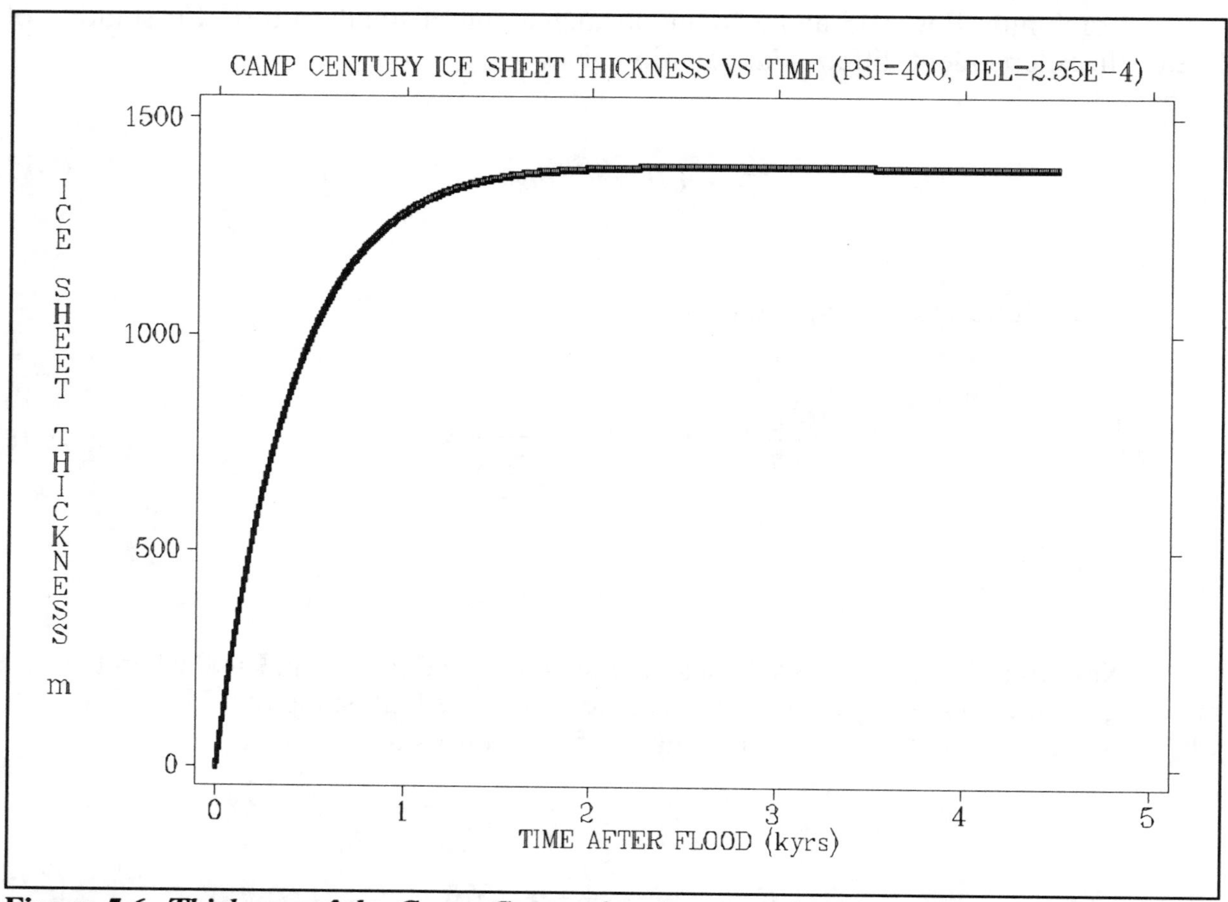


**Figure 5.6** ***Thickness of the Camp Century ice sheet as a function of time after the Flood.***

Fig. 5.6 illustrates the behavior of the entire thickness of the ice sheet, and deals primarily with the topmost layer. However, when ice cores are drilled down through the ice sheet today, we can measure the position of earlier layers which were formed and then buried. This additional information should help us develop a better estimate of the thinning function.

If we consider a given layer within the ice sheet, can we determine how far it has moved downward since it was formed? If we assume that the rate of movement downward of an ice layer is proportional to the thickness of the ice sheet and the position of a layer relative to the total thickness, we obtain:

$$V_y = \frac{dy}{dt} = -\delta \frac{y}{H_0} H(t) \tag{5.21}$$

where $V_y$ is the vertical velocity of an ice layer relative to the base of the ice sheet, y is the position of a layer, $\delta$ is the thinning ratio defined earlier, H is the total thickness of the ice sheet as a function of time, and $H_0$ is the total thickness today.

Now, at first, one might be tempted to define the downward velocity of a layer as proportional to the thickness of ice above the layer. However, it should be noted that the weight of the entire ice sheet is responsible for the movement of a given layer, because the rate at which the ice beneath a layer thins, allowing the layer to move downward, is dependent on the total thickness. Obviously, the preferable manner of deriving $V_y$ would be to have a complete, time-dependent flow model showing the full two-dimensional movement of ice as a function of depth. This is not easily determined, so my model will assume a simple relationship for this first effort.

Equation 5.21 says that the velocity of a layer is downward following its deposition and is proportional to the total thickness of the ice sheet. However, the factor, $y/H_0$, causes the downward velocity to increase linearly from 0 at the bottom of the ice sheet to a maximum at the top. The bottom must be 0, because it rests on bedrock. The upper layers will subside faster, because of the accumulating compression.

Transposing Equation 5.21 results in:

$$\frac{dy}{y} = -\delta\frac{H(t)}{H_0}dt \qquad \textbf{(5.22)}$$

Substituting H(t) from Equation 5.18 and integrating to find the change in position, y, of an ice layer over the period of time since it was laid down, $\Delta t = t_{today} - t_{deposition}$ gives:

$$\int_{y_i}^{y}\frac{dy}{y} = -\int_0^{\Delta t}\frac{\delta}{H_0}\left[\frac{\lambda_H}{\tau\delta}(1 - e^{-\delta\tau}) + \frac{9\lambda_H}{\tau(\delta - \frac{1}{\psi})}(e^{\frac{-t}{\psi}} - e^{-\delta t})\right]dt \qquad \textbf{(5.23)}$$

where $y_i$ is the initial position of the layer when it was deposited and y is the position of the layer as a function of time after it was deposited.

Solving for y:

$$y = y_i \, e^{-\frac{\delta}{H_0}\left[\frac{\lambda_H}{\tau\delta}A + \frac{9\lambda_H}{\tau(\delta - \frac{1}{\psi})}B\right]} \tag{5.24}$$

where:

$$A = \Delta t + \frac{1}{\delta}(e^{-\delta\Delta t} - 1)$$

$$B = -\frac{1}{\psi}(e^{\frac{-\Delta t}{\psi}} - 1) + \frac{1}{\delta}(e^{-\delta\Delta t} - 1)$$

Note that Equation 5.24 says that $y = y_i$ for $\Delta t = 0$. This means that the topmost layer, which is deposited today, 4,500 years after the Flood, has not yet begun to subside. Because the first layer at the end of the Flood was deposited at the position, $y_i = 0$, its position, y, will always be equal to 0. Between the Flood and today, each layer will subside a varying amount, dependent upon the total thickness of the ice sheet, its position relative to the bottom of the sheet, and the length of time from its deposition until today.

Fig. 5.7 shows the position of the layers at Camp Century as a function of time since the Flood. The curve shows the greatest rate of change in layer position during the first 1,000 years after the Flood. This is due to the large change in snowfall rate immediately after the Flood. The decrease in accumulation was assumed to be exponential with a 400 year e-folding time. The top layer of the ice sheet will be precipitated at smaller increments above the preceeding layers, and will be particularly noticeable immediately after the Flood. The curve is slightly concave upward during the last 3,000 years or so. This is due to the decreasing period of time available for the ice sheet to thin, as the top of the ice sheet is approached. At the very top, the most recent layer has not had time to thin at all, and its position is the same as the thickness of the ice sheet.

The curve in Fig. 5.7 can be used to estimate the age of the ice as a function of depth. Unfortunately, Equation 5.24, which is the basis of Fig. 5.7, will not allow $\Delta$t, the period of time back to the formation of a layer, to be solved analytically. If one wishes to determine the age of a layer at a known depth, either the age can be determined graphically from Fig. 5.7 or a Runge-Kutta numerical analysis method can be applied to Equation 5.24.

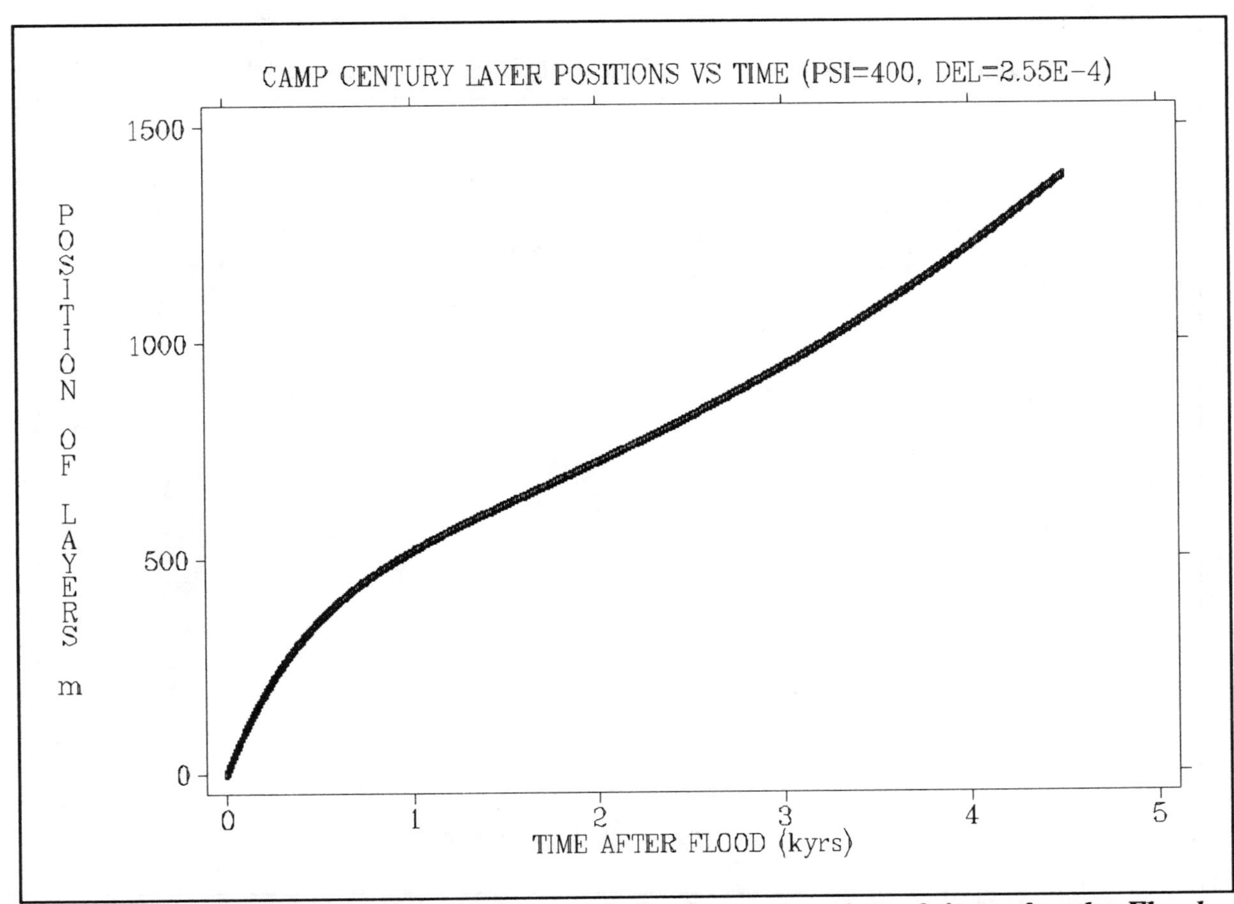


**Figure 5.7** ***Position of ice layers at Camp Century as a function of time after the Flood.***

Now that we have a young-earth model for the age of ice as a function of depth, it can be applied to the $\delta^{18}O$ data from Camp Century. The Runge-Kutta method was used on Equation 5.24 and applied to the $\delta^{18}O$ data in Fig. 5.4. The result is shown in Fig. 5.8. Note, that the general shape of the curve of $\delta^{18}O$ versus the young-earth model time has the same general shape as the curve of $\delta^{18}O$ versus depth. This is in major contrast to that of the long-age model, which compresses the data near the top of the ice sheet and dramatically stretches the data near the bottom.

If the Flood occurred 4,500 years ago, as suggested in this model, there would have been a quick "Ice Age" of about 500 years. The $\delta^{18}O$ would have decreased from a high value at the end of the Flood to a minimum about 200-300 years later. The $\delta^{18}O$ would have then increased rapidly from this minimum to the stable Holocene period in about 50 years. This latter change is in excellent agreement with the 40-year transition period of the Younger Dryas to the pre-boreal boundary suggested by Hammer et al. (1986).

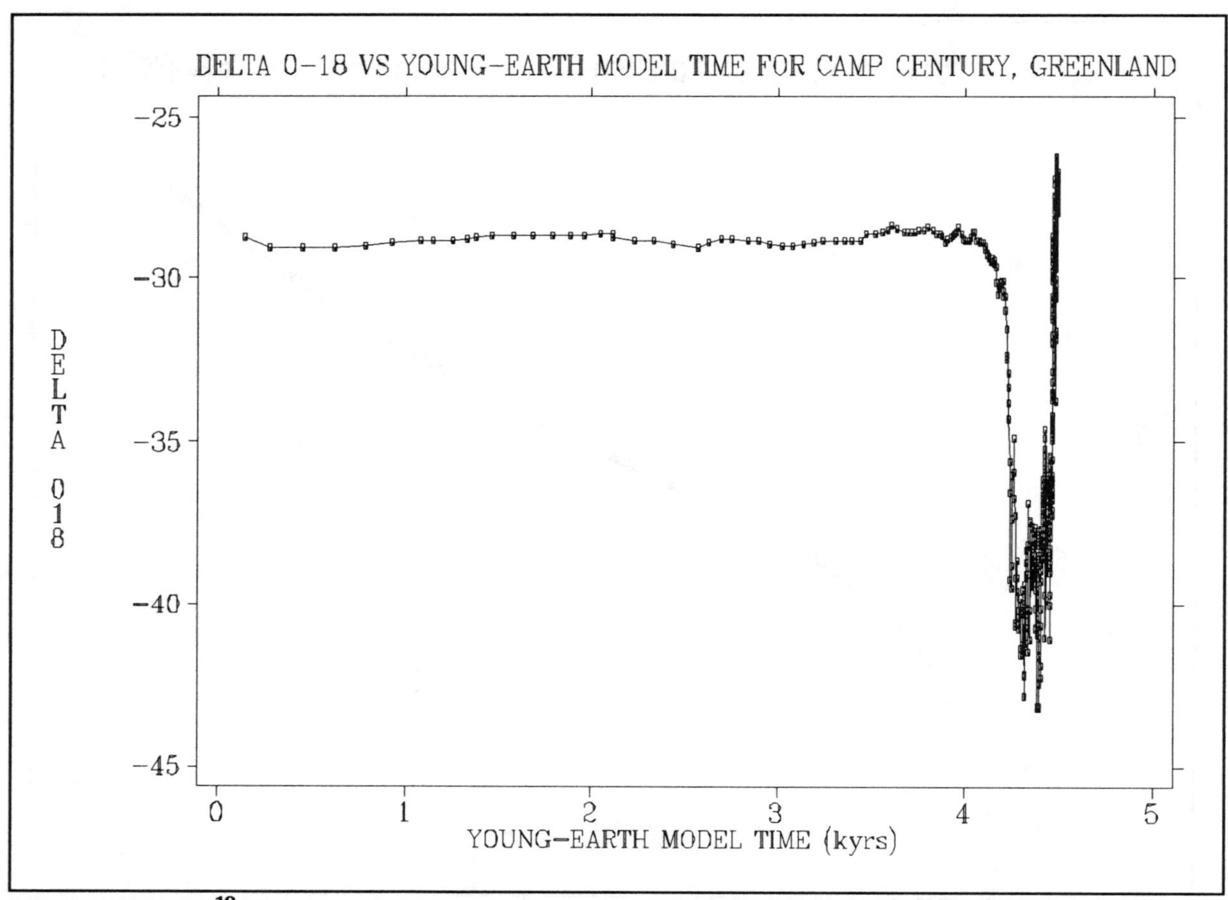


**Figure 5.8** ***$\delta^{18}O$ versus young-earth model time after the Flood for Camp Century, Greenland.***

Fig. 5.8 is the result of assuming a relatively high precipitation rate following the Flood about 4,500 years ago. Several additional parameters were incorporated into the model, most of which were determined by given boundary conditions. However, it may be possible to derive an equally valid model with different assumptions. For example, if the Flood is assumed to have occurred 14,000 years ago, as Aardsma (1991) has suggested, the model would likely assume a slightly different form.

Detailed confirmation of this model was not attempted in this report. Such an effort would require considerably more research than is reported here. The purpose of this report is to lay the general framework of an alternative model and demonstrate that a young-earth model can be formulated. One of the next efforts needed to improve this model should be to compare the observable annual layers in the upper portion of the ice sheet with the model predictions. Adjustments will likely need to be made to the parameterization based on the degree of fit between observations and predictions. Another major effort should be the development of a non-steady-state flow model. The current one-dimensional compression model may be correct, but will likely need refinement. Finally, the model should be expanded to explain other sites on Greenland and Antarctica. Of particular interest will be the forthcoming data from the Greenland Ice Sheet Project (GISP).

Even with all the caveates about the current model and hopes for improvements in the future, it seems likely that Fig. 5.8 is closer to reality than the long-age plot shown in Fig. 5.5, if the creation was recent and followed by a global flood. At the least, the young-earth model presented here is a legitimate alternative to the long-age model. It is internally consistent and capable of validation or refutation.

# CHAPTER 6

## REINTERPRETING THE RECORD

In Chapter 3, a considerable amount of time was spent describing the standard interpretation of the ice core record and how the most recent "ice age" has been understood. In that discussion, several unsolved problems in the standard interpretation were uncovered. Three of these were problems with dating the "old" ice at the bottom of the cores, the lack of correspondence between the Antarctic and Greenland records, and the sudden warming at the end of the Younger Dryas between 1200 m and 1100 m.

By approaching the ice-core data from a completely different perspective, namely, the polar ice having been deposited following a recent worldwide Flood described in the Bible, most of the problems seem to have a solution. In this chapter, an alternative model of ice-sheet formation will be described. It seems to explain several of the unsolved problems remaining in the standard interpretation. Most of my effort will be spent explaining how a worldwide adjustment in climate following the Flood could produce the sudden change in $\delta^{18}O$ observed at the end of the Younger Dryas. Coincident with this discussion, the problems of dating at the bottom of the cores and correspondence of records between the two hemispheres will be treated.

Fig. 6.1 shows the $\delta^{18}O$ distribution, with depth, at Camp Century, Greenland, displayed earlier in Chapter 5. It is evident that some process caused $\delta^{18}O$ to decrease from about -27‰ near the bottom of the core to about -40‰ near 1200 m. Quite suddenly, it then increased to about -30‰ by 1100 m and slowly stabilized at about -29‰ throughout the remainder of the core.

Because of the good theoretical and laboratory relationship between $\delta^{18}O$ and temperature, these trends have been explained as a result of temperature change. However, the more fundamental cause of such a temperature change has not been successfully described, particularly the large, rapid increase in temperature necessary to explain the sudden increase in $\delta^{18}O$ between 1200 and 1100 m. If, however, it is assumed that the worldwide Flood of Genesis 6-9 occurred in the recent past, it may be possible to successfully explain these changes in $\delta^{18}O$.

The catastrophic events of the Flood described in Genesis 6-9 are almost unimaginable. In order for man and all land-breathing animals to have been destroyed in the Flood, the entire surface of the earth would have been devastated. The layers of sedimentary rock covering most of the earth and containing millions of fossils are mute testimony to this event. Scripture says that flood waters covered the highest mountains. If this was the case, many other major geological events also occurred: Mountains rose up and valleys were carved out by receding flood waters; volcanoes spewed lava and dust over vast areas; forests were buried, and earthquakes and tidal waves swept the earth. Even the continents may have been broken apart during or shortly following the Flood.

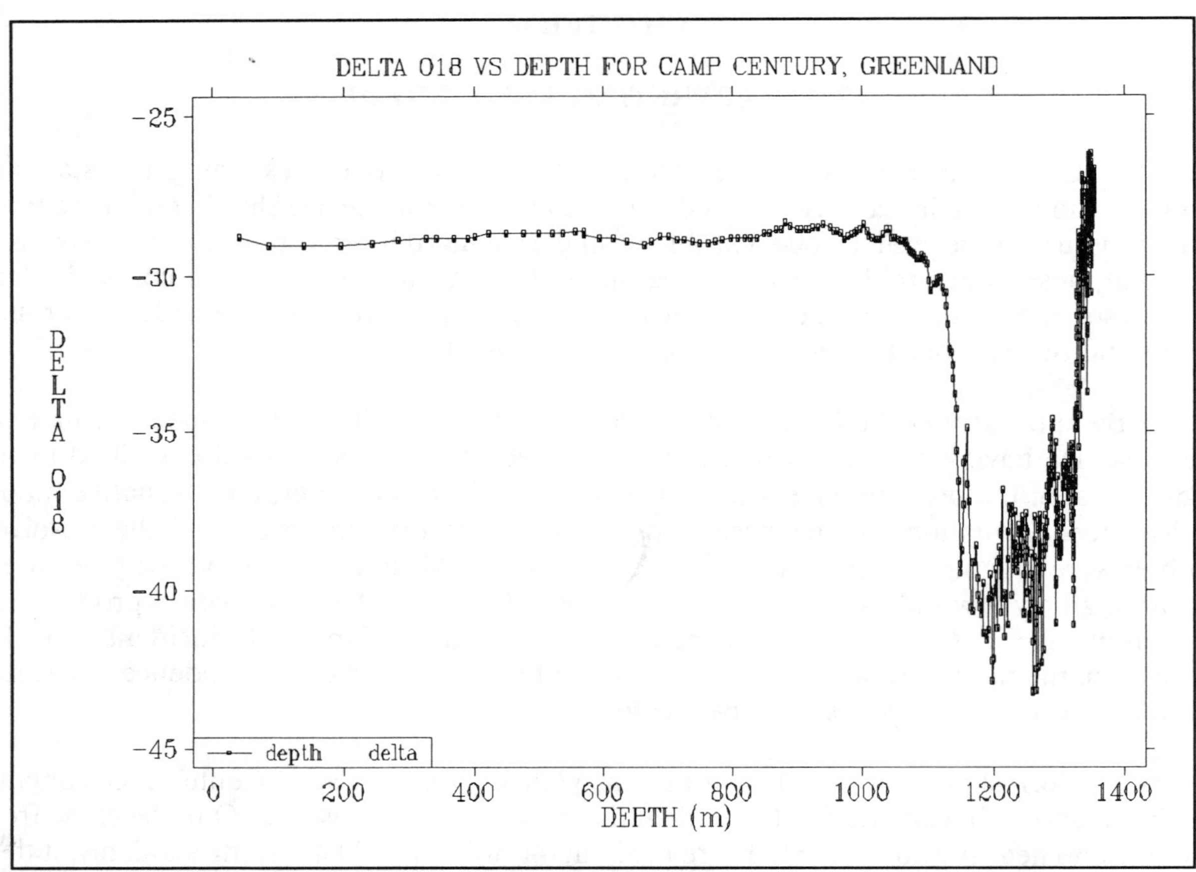


**Figure 6.1 $\delta^{18}O$ *versus depth for Camp Century, Greenland.***

The amount of energy released during these events would have resulted in significant warming of the oceans (Oard, 1990). Heat released by the collapse of the waters above the earth, present before the Flood, and by magma and warm, sub-surface waters during the Flood, would have raised the average temperature of the oceans by possibly tens of degrees above that of today. Not only would the oceans have been warmer, but because of all the mixing, they probably would have been relatively uniform in temperature from top to bottom and from equator to pole. This is not true today. The oceans are colder near the poles and at the bottom.

The Biblical description of the pre-Flood world gives the impression of a relatively warm environment, with no rain or storms. If this is true, it is likely that no ice sheets existed at the poles prior to the Flood. However, even if they were in existence before the Flood, they would have melted or have been destroyed during the Flood. Even in polar regions today, vast sedimentary rock layers exist below the ice and extend upward in isolated outcroppings called nunataks, testifying to the worldwide effects of the Flood.

Following the main deluge, many of the geologic processes did not cease abruptly, but, rather, decreased slowly in intensity and frequency, much like aftershocks following a major earthquake. Volcanoes probably continued to release dust and gases into the upper atmosphere for many years after the Flood, causing a pall over the entire earth. The observation of high concentrations of calcium, magnesium, and silicon in the lowest layers in the ice cores may be a reflection of these residual volcanic eruptions. This cover of volcanic dust and gases probably affected the radiation balance over the earth, which caused greater cooling over continents and polar regions than we experience today.

The contrast between warm oceans and cold continents probably resulted in intense storminess along coastlines. A description of the effects of the Flood on the formation of an "ice age" is ably described in Oard (1990). He discusses, in great detail, causes of an "ice age;" the beginning, progression, and ending of an "ice age;" and evidences for a single "ice age" rather than many. However, Oard (1990) does not treat the evidence gleaned from ice cores, which would support such an alternative model, nor does he describe, in detail, the general circulation which would likely be associated with such a model. I will attempt to do so here.

The general circulation of the atmosphere, as it is observed and understood today, is shown in Fig. 6.2. It is essentially a three-celled Hadley circulation modified by the Coriolis forces on a rotating earth (Lorenz, 1967). The earth is observed to be in thermal equilibrium, but net radiational cooling occurs at the poles, and net warming occurs near the equator. To balance the thermal heat source at the equator with the heat sinks at the poles, the ocean and atmosphere transport heat from the equator to the poles.

The cells in the atmosphere nearest the equator cause air to rise over the equator and flow toward the poles, then descend near 30° latitude. In the Northern Hemisphere, air is deflected to the right of its path by the Coriolis force, so that the northeast trade winds are created as the descending air moves back toward the equator at the surface. The following descriptions generally refer to the Northern-Hemisphere patterns. Directions of air flow are opposite in the Southern Hemisphere.

In the rising air near the equator, clouds form, and heavy precipitation falls along a belt around the globe called the intertropical convergence zone, or the equatorial low. This zone is centered over the equator, but moves northward in the Northern Hemisphere's summer and southward during the winter. Its passage northward and southward over certain regions is amplified by the terrain and local monsoons. When the ascending part of the cell is over, or north of a tropical location in the northern hemisphere, the weather is rainy and humid; when it is south of the location, the weather is hot and dry.

Near 30° latitude, where the air routinely descends, few, if any, clouds form, and desert conditions persist in a belt surrounding the earth. The southwestern U.S., Mexico, the Sahara Desert in North Africa, Saudi Arabia, and Iran are all arid regions caused by this descending air. This desert condition persists even over the ocean at this latitude. These regions are called the horse latitudes, or doldrums, because little or no wind occurs, as well as little rain. This region forms a subtropical high.

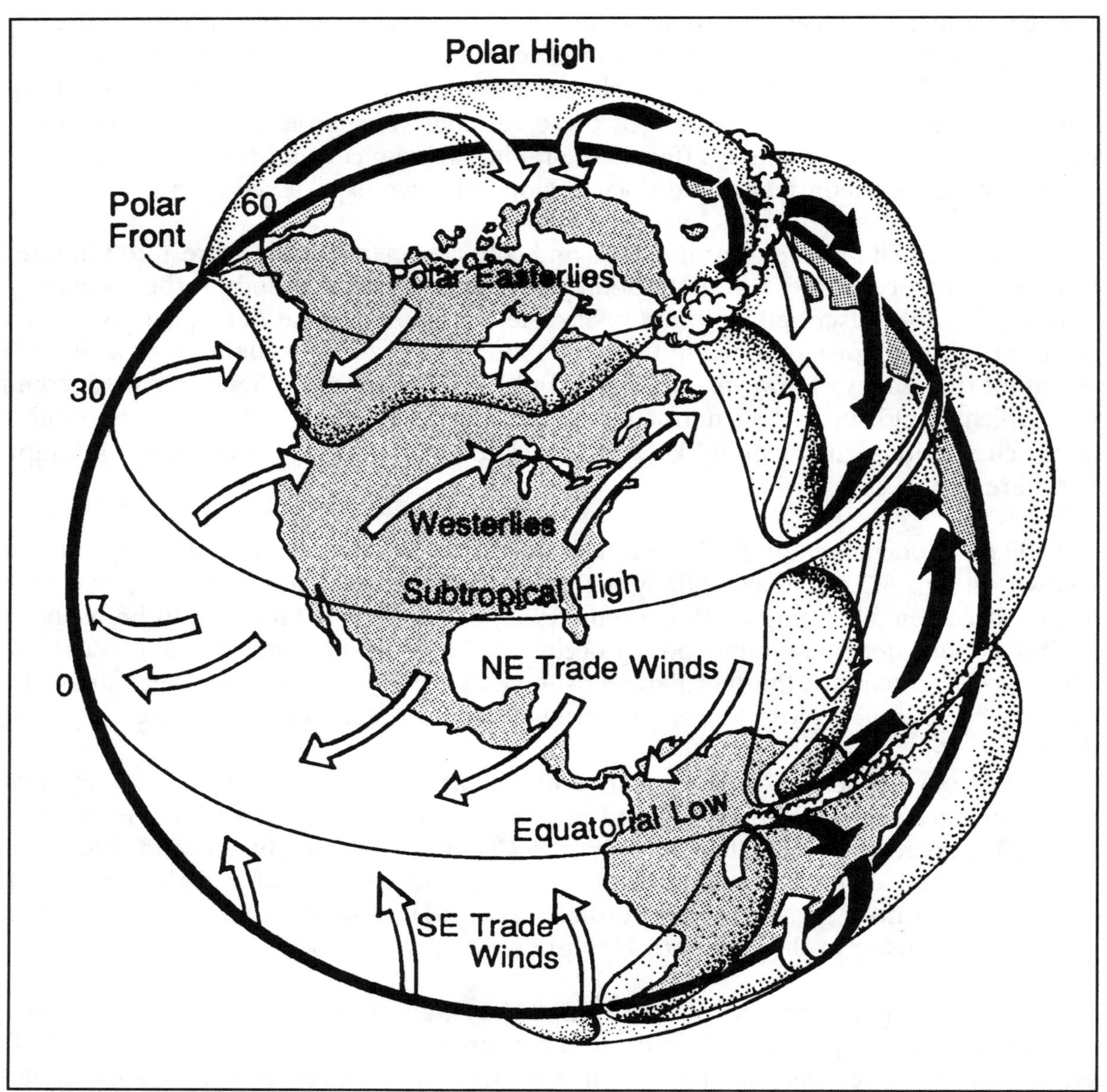


**Figure 6.2** ***The general circulation of today's atmosphere. Light arrows show air flow at the surface and dark arrows aloft.***

Between the subtropical high and the polar front further to the north, westerlies prevail. This region is characterized by winds blowing from the west, as surface air moves north from the subtropical high and is deflected to the right. It is also characterized by stormy weather, particularly in the winter, as storms circle the globe along the polar front. The polar front is a sharp discontinuity in air temperature between the cold polar-air mass and the warmer mid-latitude air. Because of this thermal temperature gradient, a high-speed belt of air aloft, called the jet-stream, travels from west to east along the polar front, circling the globe. The polar front and its associated jet stream oscillate north and south, depending on the season of the year and the intensity of a particular storm traveling along the polar front. Cloudiness and precipitation at a location in mid-latitudes depend strongly on how frequently the polar front approaches and remains over a given locale with its attendant storminess.

Over the pole, air descends, as heat is removed by radiation to space. The cold air at the surface moves southward toward the polar front and is deflected to the right, forming polar easterlies. Cold air is more dense than warmer air, and forms high pressure. It also tends to hug the ground and slide under the warmer air to the south, lifting any moisture available to form clouds and precipitation along the polar front. Significant quantities of snow and ice can form near the polar front, if the interface between the two air masses remains fixed at a given location for an extended period. Under the polar high, relatively few clouds and little precipitation form. What precipitation does occur remains in a frozen state for long periods of time.

Now, how would this picture likely have been different in the past immediately following the Flood, when circumstances were considerably different, and where non-equilibrium conditions prevailed? The following scenario is a first attempt at developing a conceptual model of the general atmospheric circulation immediately after the Flood, as the ocean/atmosphere system transitioned from an initially uniform temperature distribution to that of today.

Fig. 6.3 shows a two-celled Hadley circulation which may have developed during the latter stages of the Flood. The most active region in the atmosphere likely would have been near the poles. The maximum radiational cooling would have occurred at high levels in the atmosphere, directly over the poles. However, at the surface, the oceans would have been warm -- possibly as warm as 30°C. Tremendous evaporation rates would have occurred from the ocean surfaces, with condensation and freezing aloft. This situation would not only be *convectively* unstable, but also also be *dynamically* unstable. The intensification and organization of convection in this scenario would be very similar to the organization of a hurricane by what is called "convective instability of the second kind," or "CISK." Essentially, intense convection will organize itself by drawing in warm surface air and humidity which is deflected by Coriolis forces into spiral rain bands.

At the center of a hurricane intense precipitation occurs and residual air is exhausted to the upper atmosphere, where it moves outward from the center of convection. The air then descends at large distances from the hurricane, producing clear skies and warm, dry regions. This intensification and organization of convection into a hurricane-like circulation with strong, gusty winds, may be what Genesis 8:1 is referring to at the end of the Flood:

> And God remembered Noah, and every living thing, and all the cattle that was with him in the ark: and God made a wind to pass over the earth, and the waters assuaged ...

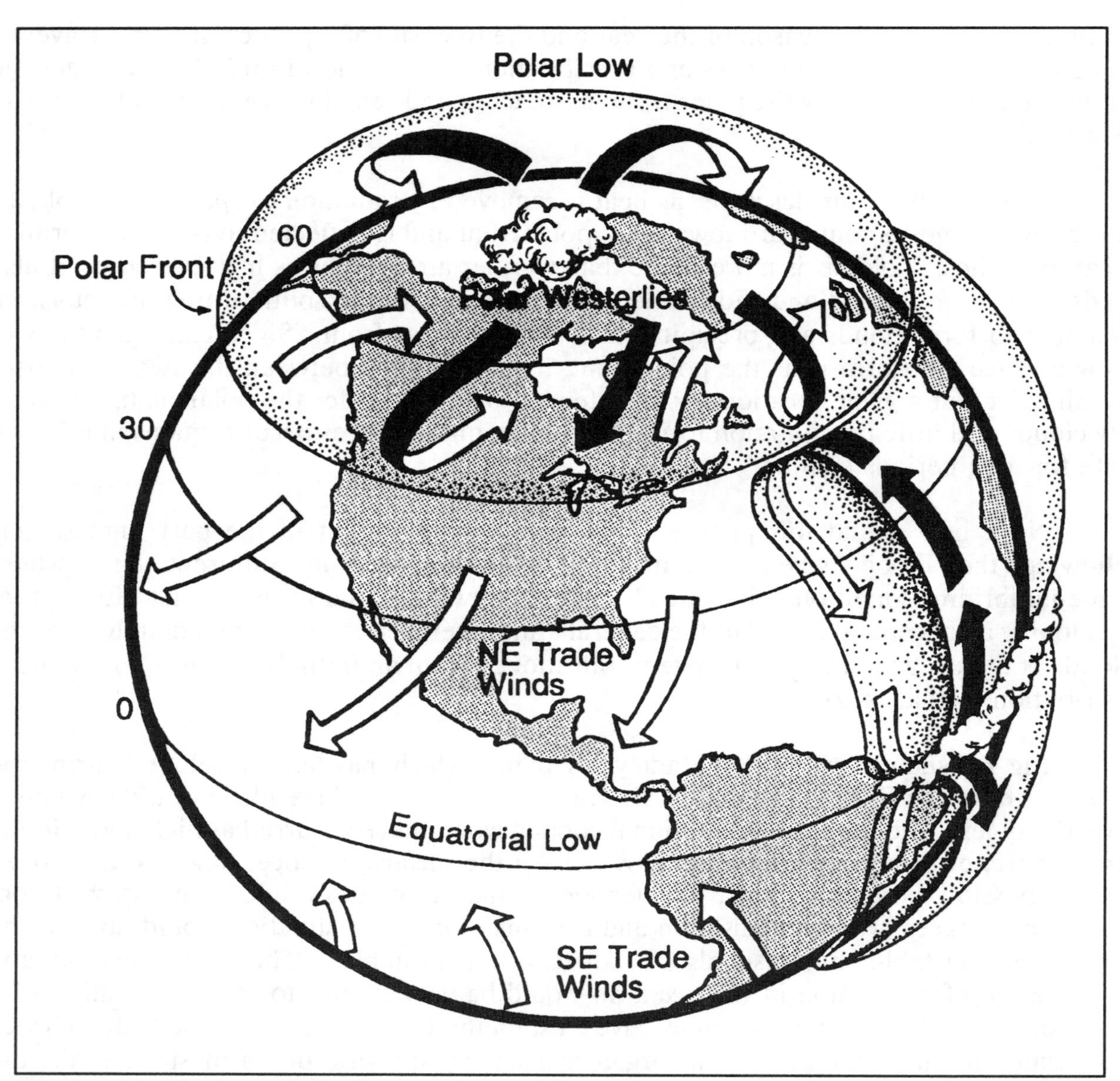


**Figure 6.3** ***The hypothetical general circulation of the atmosphere soon after the Flood. Warm oceans and large rates of radiational cooling over the poles would drive extreme convection.***

Fig. 6.4 shows an example of a hurricane -- in this case, Hurricane Gladys in the Gulf of Mexico during 1968. Hurricane Gladys filled the entire gulf with spiral rain bands from the coast of Mexico to the Florida peninsula. Fig. 6.5 shows a diagram of air motions in such a hurricane relative to the spiral rain bands and the storm center. The typical hurricane contains rainbands spiraling around a central eye. The center-most rainband contains the strongest winds and heaviest precipitation. Descending air typically occurs in the eye, producing clearing, cessation of precipitation, and weak winds. The main difference

**Figure 6.4** *Hurricane Gladys in the Gulf of Mexico during 1968 (NASA).*

in the scenario I am proposing from that of a typical hurricane, is the scale and intensity of the system. Initially, the storm centered on the pole may have been the size of a typical hurricane, but would have rapidly expanded to cover a major portion of the hemisphere.

In Fig. 6.3, the storm over the northern hemisphere is shown to draw warm, moist air from as far away as 45° latitude. At the surface, all the winds would be westerlies, feeding into the storm center at the pole. Aloft, the winds would be easterlies, as the air

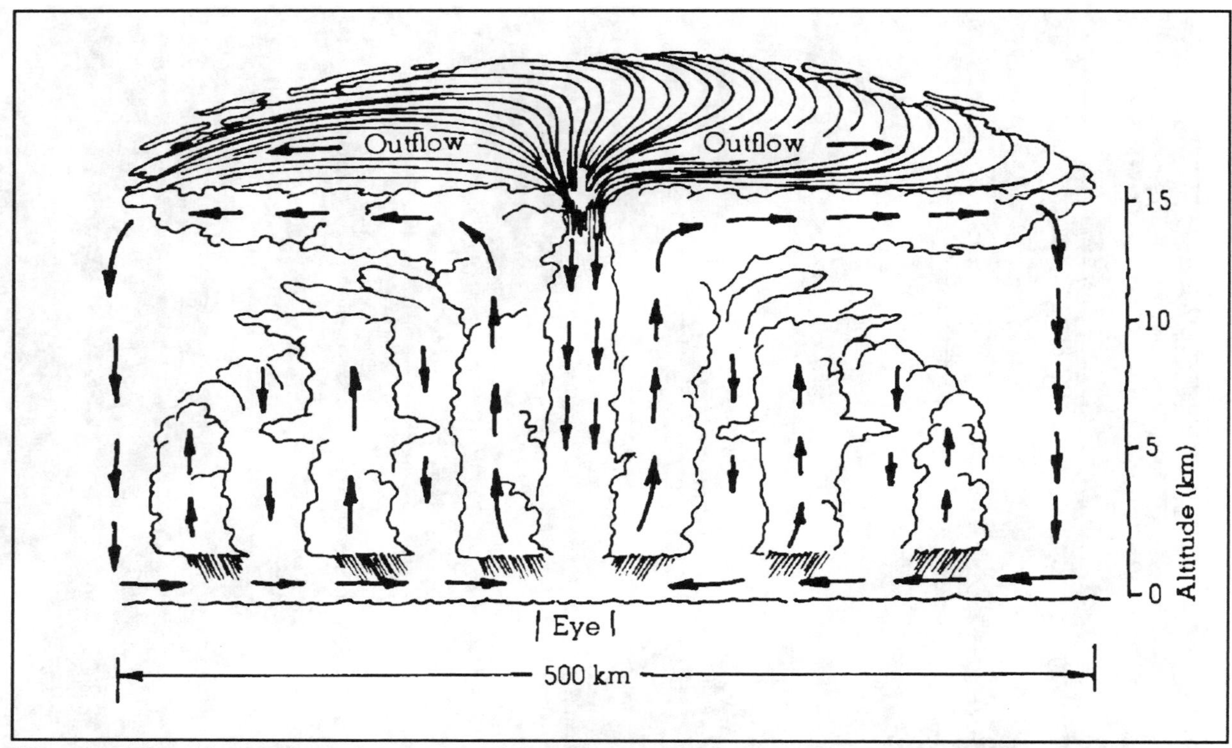


**Figure 6.5** *Air motions in a typical hurricane relative to spiral rain bands and the storm center (Ahrens, 1988).*

diverges from the storm center. At the periphery of the storm, the air descends to make another circuit toward the pole at the surface. Less cloudiness or precipitation would have occurred here, even though the oceans were warm. Near the equator, an equatorial low, similar to that of today with rising air, clouds, and precipitation would have occurred. It is likely that the intensity of the circulation would have been greater, however, and with more precipitation.

As the polar storm continued to intensify, it is likely that it developed an eye, such as in a modern hurricane. An eye in a hurricane is a region in the center of a storm where the air is descending. The eye develops because, as the wind speed increases, the Coriolis force deflects the winds spiraling toward the center to such a degree that they become concentric with the center before they reach it. An eye wall forms some distance from the center, where most of the condensation, precipitation, and updraft occur. Air is drawn from the eye near the surface to feed the updraft in the eye wall, and, consequently, is generally descending in the eye. A similar, but larger system probably occurred over the poles as the storm continued to intensify. As it intensified, the precipitation formed a ring around the poles which moved southward and expanded in size. In addition, the storm continued to draw warm, moist air from greater distances to the south -- even possibly south of 30° latitude, as shown in Fig. 6.6.

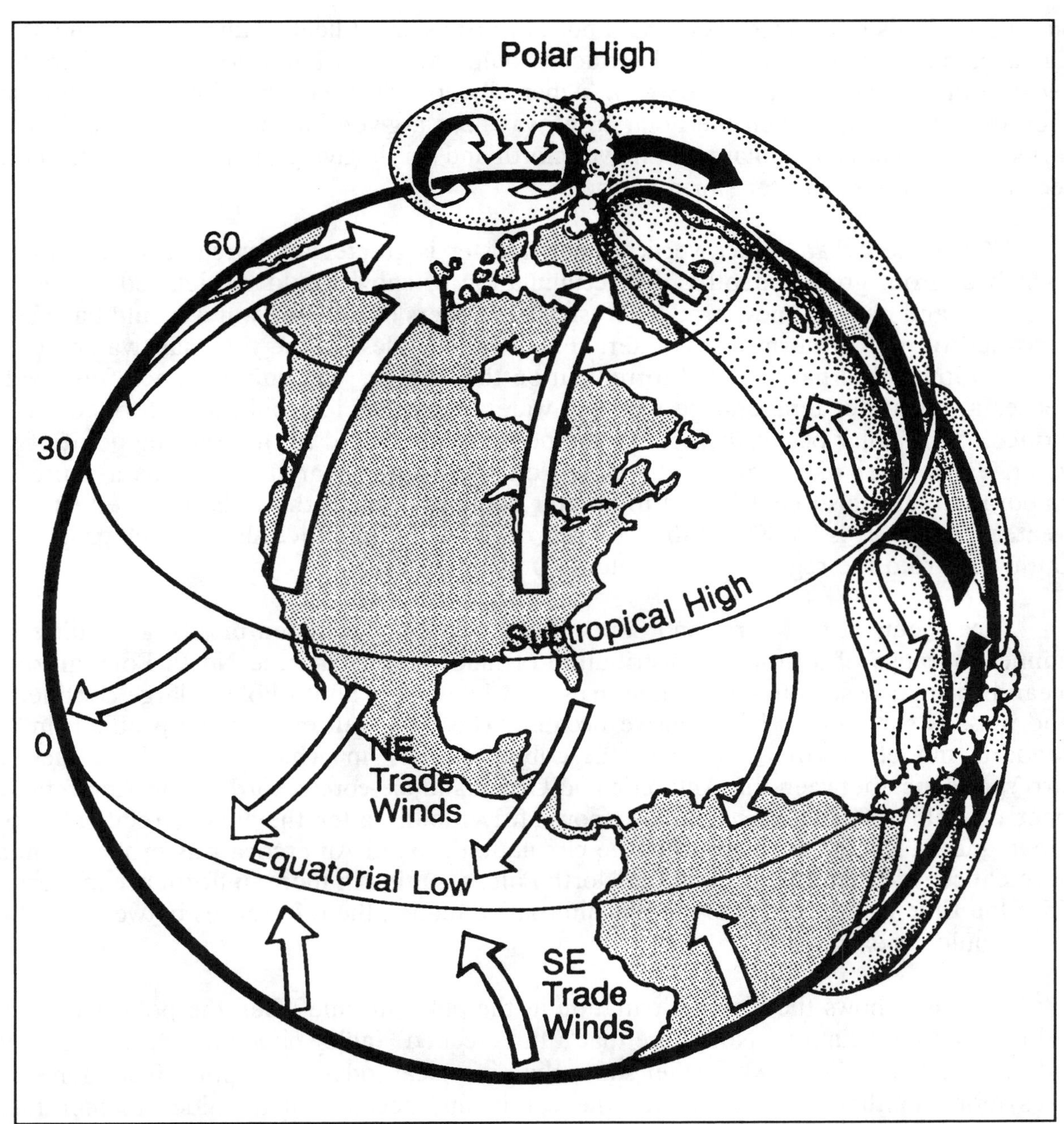


**Figure 6.6** ***Intense stage of general circulation development over the pole. This stage probably occurred within 100 years or less of the Flood. Note the development of an "eye."***

As long as the precipitation remained as rain, the polar storm described above acted very much like a large, intense hurricane. However, at some point, the oceans and atmosphere had given up enough heat that the precipitation in the ring around the pole turned to snow. The timing of this has been estimated by Oard (1990) to be on the order of 500 years or so after the Flood. More modeling needs to be done to provide better estimates of the time frame. However, once snow began to fall, it would have accumulated on land surfaces first, since they would not have transferred heat readily to melt the snow. The accumulation of snow on land surfaces would have contributed to the rate of cooling, because of the radiational effects of a higher albedo. The accumulation rate could have been extremely high, when the polar front was near a given location. It also could have varied somewhat as the polar front moved north and south, giving the impression of annual accumulations over shorter storm periods.

Over the oceans, since vertical heat transfer is greater and circulation could draw upon heat from greater depths, the accumulation of snow would be delayed somewhat. Since rain and melting snow produce fresh water, layers of salt-free water would have been deposited on top of normal sea water. Fresh water is less dense than salt water, so the precipitation would have tended to remain on the surface. In addition, since fresh water freezes at a warmer temperature than salt water, a layer of ice could have formed on the surface of the polar oceans before the temperature decreased to the freezing point of sea water. This layer of ice eventually closed off the oceans near the poles as a source of evaporation, and also contributed to greater cooling, through the radiational effects of a greater albedo. It is likely that the ice layer developed into an ice shelf, which progressed southward from the region of most-intense precipitation.

Ice sheets at the North and South Poles probably developed in a slightly different manner, because of a different distribution of land masses. At the North Pole, an open ocean is primarily surrounded by land masses, while at the South Pole, a large continental land mass is surrounded by extensive oceans. This may well explain the problem in the standard model of the "ice ages" described earlier, in which there is a lack of correspondence between the Antarctic and Greenland ice-core records. The Antarctic ice sheet probably began to accumulate snow fairly rapidly after the Flood, relative to the Greenland ice sheet. Furthermore, the circulation around Antarctica was probably much more concentric than that around the North Pole, resulting in more uniform accumulation. Since the time frame is so short in this alternative model, the differences between the two poles would be exaggerated.

Fig. 6.7 shows the global circulation at the point in time when the polar ice sheets had reached a maximum. Note here that a three-celled Hadley circulation has developed, and the polar front is shown further south than is typical today. The polar front generally takes more southerly positions over the continents, because their colder temperatures combine with warm ocean temperatures to induce large standing waves in the general circulation. These standing waves tend to cause more northerly flow over the continents and more southerly flow over the oceans. The oceans then become major sources of heat and moisture to the polar and continental regions. Evidence from moraines at the edge of glaciers, and sea-floor sediments beneath the edges of ice shelves, show that in the past, an ice shelf extended south of 45° latitude in the North Atlantic. The polar front probably skirted just south of the ice shelf.

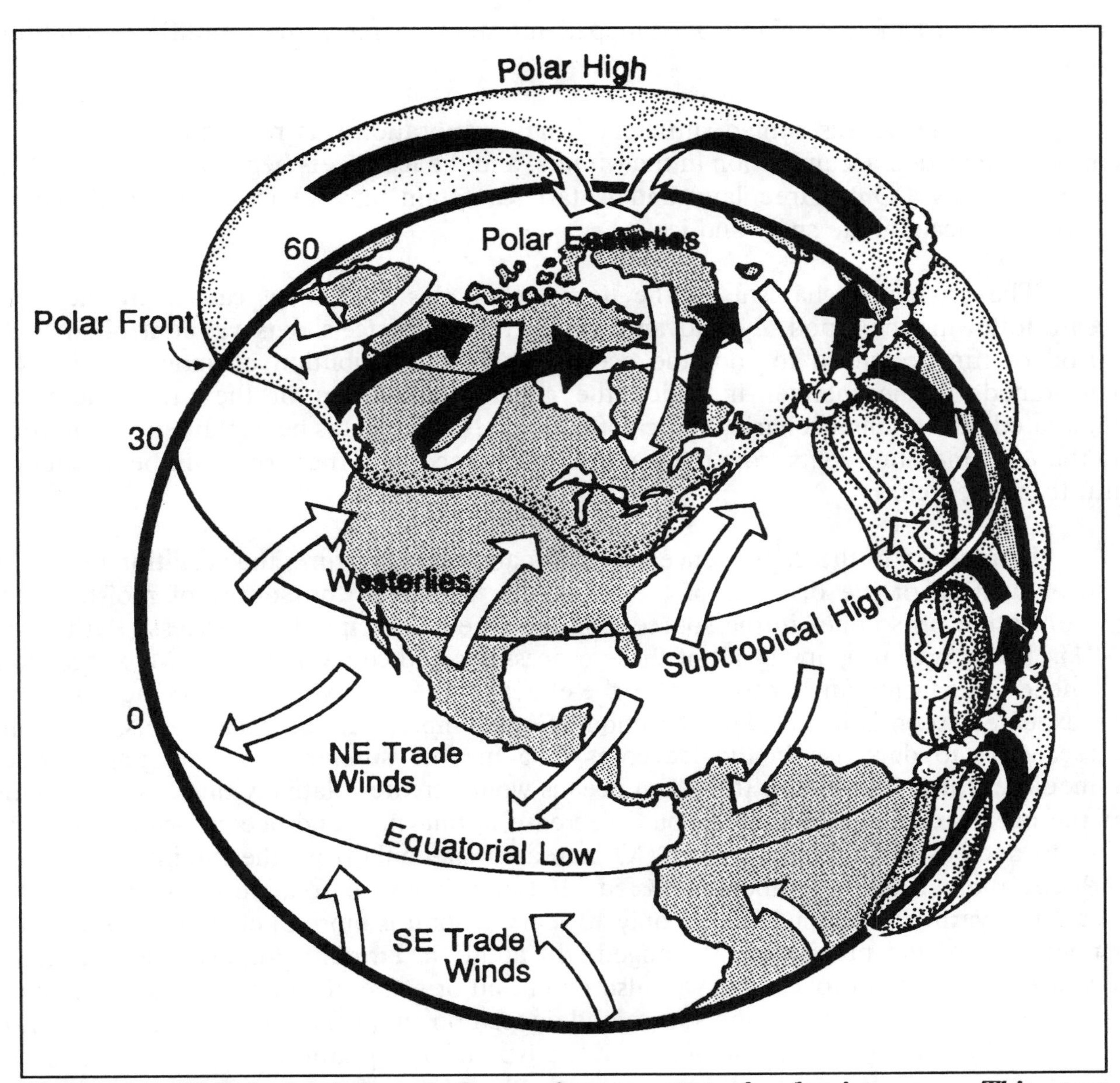


**Figure 6.7** *Global circulation at the maximum extent of polar ice caps. This stage probably occurred 500 to 1000 years after the Flood. Note the three-celled Hadley circulation.*

The ice shelf apparently did not extend as far south in the Pacific Ocean as it did in the Atlantic; however, a shelf in the Southern Hemisphere appears to have extended northward from Antarctica to near the tip of South America, and may have reached South Africa and the southern tip of Australia. As the oceans cooled and more of the ocean surface was covered with ice, the active precipitation zones moved further equatorward. The jet streams in both hemispheres probably tended to follow the edge of the ice sheets, since this was where the major north-south temperature gradient occurred. The massive ice sheets poleward of the polar fronts capped moisture sources, and amplified radiational cooling.

Once the oceans cooled sufficiently that evaporation was reduced, melting in the summers exceeded accumulation in the winters, and the ice sheets began to recede to those observed today. Only Greenland and Antarctica retain massive ice sheets and actually continue to accumulate snow and ice.

The driving mechanism for the "Ice Age" in this model was caused by the warm oceans following the Flood. The advance and retreat of the ice sheets was controlled by the period of time required to cool the oceans, and the distribution of snow and ice was determined by the manner in which the general circulation of the atmosphere was modulated. Given this scenario, how can the features in ice cores be explained? I will focus on the $\delta^{18}O$ measurements from the Camp Century record. Other cores will be considered in future research.

In addition to the dependence upon formation temperature, the variation of $\delta^{18}O$ is also a function of the distance of the deposition site from the source of moisture, the concentration of isotopes in the source, and the type of precipitation process (Petit et al., 1981). In my scenario, any or all of these processes could come into play. My suggestions will need to be tested further to quantify the effects; however, I will determine here whether the expected trend is in the right direction. For example: As the ocean cools, we would expect $\delta^{18}O$ to decrease in the ice cores in a manner similar to the long-age model. Immediately after the Flood, the warm oceans would create relatively thick, warm clouds. As the oceans cooled, the clouds would decrease in thickness and become colder, causing $\delta^{18}O$ to decrease. However, when $\delta^{18}O$ increased suddenly from the minimum of about -40‰ at about 1200 m, to about -30‰ at 1100 m, it is not reasonable to assume that the ocean had warmed by about 15°C in only 40 years or so; it is more likely that the formation temperature of the precipitation changed. In addition, I would propose that the major decrease from 1370 m to 1200 m was also due to all or some of three other processes: (1) a change in distance between the source and deposition site; (2) a change in concentration of $\delta^{18}O$ at the source; and (3) a change in the type of precipitation.

Once the snow began to accumulate over the ocean after the Flood, an ice shelf developed, similar to what happens, in a more limited degree in winter today, as shown in Fig. 6.8. The ice shelf covered sources of moisture close to the Camp Century site on Greenland. As the shelf continued to grow southward, the source region for moisture moved further away, lowering the expected value of $\delta^{18}O$. Precipitation over the open ocean south of the ice shelf also remained on the surface, diluting the sea water with fresh water already reduced in $\delta^{18}O$ by a previous cycle of evaporation and precipitation, thus producing a further lowering of $\delta^{18}O$.

The intensity of the precipitation process would be greatest near the polar front, which typically would coincide with the edge of the ice shelf over the ocean. Intense

**Figure 6.8** *The Ross ice shelf in the Antarctic (Scott, 1911).*

precipitation processes are more likely to involve condensation-coalescence processes, which would be expected to have higher values of $\delta^{18}O$. The condensation-coalescence process involves the formation of cloud droplets on condensation nuclei followed by the collision and coalescence of a few of the largest droplets and subsequent precipitation of rain. It is a liquid phase change only, and consequently causes only small fractionation of the isotopes of oxygen. As the ice shelf and associated polar front moved further away from Camp Century, the type of precipitation more likely would result from a less-intense sublimation-nucleation precipitation process, with lower values of $\delta^{18}O$.

This sublimation-nucleation process involves formation of ice crystals on ice nuclei followed by depositional growth from the vapor, and subsequent precipitation of snow. It is a solid phase change only, and, consequently, causes large fractionation of the isotopes of oxygen. Intermediate between these two extremes is the sublimation-nucleation at high levels in a cloud followed by riming lower in the cloud, as ice crystals collect liquid water on their fall to the ground. This type of precipitation could be extremely heavy, and would produce moderate fractionation of the isotopes of oxygen.

We can therefore explain the trend toward lower values of $\delta^{18}O$ between 1370 m and 1200 m with our alternative model, with or without a large temperature change. The actual change in average ocean temperature may be more closely related to the difference in $\delta^{18}O$

value between 1370 m and 1000 m. If all other processes are assumed to be the same at 1370 m and 1000 m, this would suggest that the average surface temperature of the ocean changed by 3°C, between the time snow began to accumulate at Camp Century and today. This is not the magnitude of temperature change normally associated with an "Ice Age." Yet, a change in average global ocean temperature of 3°C would still produce a major effect on global climate.

But what about the sudden change from 1200 m to 1100 m? I propose that once the ocean cooled sufficiently and the ice sheets on the continents and ice shelves on the oceans stopped growing, the ice shelves began to retreat rapidly. Ice shelves around Antarctica and in the North Sea are observed to break up very quickly in the spring today -- much more rapidly than they form. In this case, the evidence seems to indicate that the retreat of the ice shelves occurred in about 40 years. The sudden retreat of the ice shelf would cause the distance between the source and deposition site to diminish, increasing the $\delta^{18}O$ rapidly. This retreat would also be associated with less precipitation on the ocean surface as the oceans cooled and increased mixing of surface waters because of melting of the ice, thereby increasing the $\delta^{18}O$ at the source. However, the type of precipitation is likely to continue to be a result of the sublimation-nucleation process, and not contribute to an increase in $\delta^{18}O$ as the shelf retreats. The first two processes could easily increase the $\delta^{18}O$ in the snow falling at Camp Century by 10‰ over a 40-year period. The long lag time needed to warm the huge mass of the oceans by 15°C, in order to increase $\delta^{18}O$ by the thermal effect only, would not be necessary.

This explanation is much more likely than the great heating needed by the traditional model. The expectation that changes in $CO_2$ concentration caused atmospheric warming, which, in turn, produced the large change of 10‰ in $\delta^{18}O$, is even more unlikely. If the change in $\delta^{18}O$ can be shown to be due to factors other than temperature, then the break up of the ice shelves is a better explanation of the $\delta^{18}O$ record at Camp Century between 1200 m and 1100 m.

## CHAPTER 7

## CONCLUSIONS AND RECOMMENDATIONS

Ice-core data can support only an undisputed chronology back several thousand years B.P. The standard long-age model calculates the age of the ice at the bottom of ice sheets to be 160,000 years old, by making uniformitarian assumptions about precipitation rates and other related variables. The standard model has been unable to explain several puzzling features in the data, such as: (1) dating problems with old ice near the bottom of the cores; (2) lack of correspondence between the Antarctic and Greenland records; and (3) sudden warming at the end of the Younger Dryas. By assuming the historicity of the worldwide Flood described in Genesis and other likely attendant geophysical processes, an alternative chronology has been developed, which is of the same order as the time frame derived from a literal interpretation of Scripture. The alternative model also has been able to explain some of the problems unsolved by the standard long-age model, and suggest plausible physical processes which produced the data.

It is evident that this alternative "Biblical" model should be tested in greater detail, to demonstrate its validity and/or to modify its components. Probably the most fertile development should occur in the area of numerical modeling. The assumptions about increased precipitation rates near the bottom of the ice sheets need to be validated, if possible, by independent data from the ice cores. The long-age model has used a relationship between temperature and $\delta^{18}O$ to predict precipitation rates near the bottom. Since I have suggested that the $\delta^{18}O$ is not dependent only on temperature, a much more complicated relationship ensues. Either such a relationship needs to be derived or another parameter needs to be identified from the ice core data which accurately predicts the precipitation rate.

Another subject which needs exploration is the circulation model developed in Chapter 6. Although the circulation suggested is reasonable by current knowledge of the atmosphere, it is a projection to conditions not experienced on Earth today. In particular, the transition from a two-celled Hadley circulation to a three-celled Hadley circulation via a hurricane-like storm development is highly conjectural. Is it possible for the eye of this global storm to enlarge to the scale of a global circulation, with a warm, low-pressure center becoming a cold, high-pressure center? This question probably could be answered by experiments on a General Circulation Model (GCM). Plans have been laid to conduct such experiments in the next few years, if funds can be obtained to purchase the computer time.

Although I have assumed the main driving force for the alternative model is the warmth of the oceans following the Flood, in agreement with Oard (1990), I have not discussed the ocean circulations. The adjustments of temperature in the oceans from a uniform distribution from top to bottom and equator to pole to today's configuration, is not a minor consideration. Because of the long time lag in the formation of cold bottom waters and saline layers, it may be possible to detect some latent information about the ocean's response to the post-Flood ice age, from the ocean itself. An examination of cold and saline layers in the ocean is well justified. It also would be valuable to use a coupled atmosphere/ocean GCM, when conducting the numerical experiments on circulation suggested earlier.

Finally, the alternative model is strongly dependent upon evidence that ice shelves formed as far south as 45° latitude in the Atlantic Ocean. Some evidence, showing the formation of ice shelves northward from Antarctica to the tip of South America, and possibly close to Australia and South Africa is also available. A full exploration of the sea-floor sediment data recently made available from CLIMAP and other oceanic research projects, is mandatory. To this end, I plan to spend the next year or so studying these data, to reinterpret and possibly extend the current view of the "ice age" from sea-floor sediment.

Nothing in the ice core data from either Greenland or Antarctica requires the earth to be tens of thousands of years old. In fact, there is good reason to believe that the ice cores are revealing important information about conditions following the Flood of Genesis and the recent formation of thick ice sheets. Reports of ice-core data containing records of climatic changes as far back as 160,000 years in the past are dependent upon interpretations of these data. Such interpretations could be seriously wrong, if the Genesis Flood occurred as described in the Bible. Further research on ice-core data should be a high priority for creationist researchers.

## REFERENCES CITED


Aardsma, G.E., 1991. **Radiocarbon and the Genesis Flood.** ICR Monograph, Institute for Creation Research, San Diego, 82 pp.

Ahrens, C.D., 1988. **Meteorology Today.** West Publishing Co., St. Paul, 582 pp.

Auer, V., 1960. **Proc. Roy. Soc.**, B, 152, 507.

Bates, T.S., R.J. Charlson, and R.H. Gammon, 1987. *Evidence for the climatic role of marine biogenic sulphur.* **Nature**, 329, 319-321.

Benson, C.S., 1959. *Physical investigation on the snow and firn of northwest Greenland, 1952, 1953, 1954.* **U.S. Army SIPRE**, Research Report 26.

Boyle, E.A., 1988a. *The role of vertical chemical fractionation in controlling late quaternary atmospheric carbon dioxide.* **J. Geophys. Res.**, 93, 15701-15714.

Boyle, E.A., 1988b. *Vertical oceanic nutrient fractionation and glacial/interglacial* $CO_2$ *cycles.* **Nature**, 331, 55-58.

Broecker, W.S. and G.H. Denton, 1989. *The role of ocean-atmosphere reorganizations in glacial cycles.* **Geochim. Cosmochim. Acta.**, 53, 2465-2501.

Broecker, W.S., D.M. Peteet, and D. Rind, 1985. *Does the ocean-atmosphere system have more than one stable mode of operation?* **Nature**, 315, 21-26.

Bryson, R.A., 1989. *Late quaternary volcanic modulation of Milankovitch climate forcing.* **Theor. Appl. Climatol.**, 39, 115-125.

Charlson, R.J., J.E. Lovelock, M.O. Andrea, and S.G. Warren, 1987. *Oceanic phytoplankton, atmospheric sulphur, cloud albedo and climate.* **Nature**, 326, 655-661.

Clausen, H.B. and C.C. Langway, Jr., 1989. *The ionic deposits in polar ice cores.* In: **The Environmental Record in Glaciers and Ice Sheets,** eds., H. Oeschger and C.C. Langway, Jr., John Wiley and Sons, Limited, New York, 225-247.

Cragoe, C.S., 1955. *Properties of ethylene glycol and its aqueous solutions.* **National Bureau of Standards**, Report #4268.

Craig, H., 1961. *Isotope variations in meteoritic waters.* **Science**, 133, 1702-1703.

Crowley, T.J. and G.R. North, 1991. ***Paleoclimatology***. **Oxford University Press**, New York, 87.

Czul, E.C. and J.J. Gennari, 1965. *Load carrying terminal for armored electric cables*. **U.S. Naval Research Laboratory**, Report #6261.

Dansgaard, W., 1964. *Stable isotopes in precipitation*. **Tellus**, 16, 436-468.

Dansgaard, W., H.B. Clausen, N. Gundestrup, C.U. Hammer, S.J. Johnsen, P.M. Kristinsdottir, and N. Reeh, 1982. *A new Greenland deep ice core*. **Science**, 218, 1273-1277.

Dansgaard, W., S.J. Johnsen, H.B. Clausen, and C.C. Langway, Jr., 1971. *Climatic record revealed by the Camp Century ice core*. In: **Late Cenozoic Glacial Ages,** ed., K.K. Turekian, Yale University Press, New Haven and London.

Dansgaard, W., S.J. Johnsen, J. Møller, and C.C. Langway, Jr., 1969. *One thousand centuries of climatic record from Camp Century on the Greenland ice sheet*. In: **Late Cenozoic Glacial Ages**, ed., K.K. Turekian, Yale University Press, New Haven and London.

Dansgaard, W. and H. Oeschger, 1989. *Past environmental long-term records from the Arctic*. In: **The Environmental Record in Glaciers and Ice Sheets**, eds., H. Oeschger and C.C. Langway, Jr., John Wiley and Sons, Limited, New York, 287-318.

Epstein, S., R.P. Sharp, and A. J. Gow, 1970. **Science**, 168, 1570.

Fisher, D., R. Koerner, W. Paterson, W. Dansgaard, N. Gundestrup, and N. Reeh, 1983. *Effect of wind scouring on climatic records from ice-core oxygen-isotope profiles*. **Nature**, 301, 205-209.

Flohn, H., 1979. *On time scales and causes of abrupt paleoclimatic events*. **Quat. Res.**, 12, 135-149.

Flohn, H., 1986. *Singular events and catastrophes now and in climatic history*. **Naturwissenschaften**, 73, 136-149.

Garfield, D.E., 1968. *Drill hole measurements at Byrd Station*. **U.S. Army Cold Regions Research and Engineering Laboratory (USA CRREL)**, Internal Report 58.

Garfield, D.E. and H.T. Ueda, 1968. *Drilling through the Greenland ice sheet*. **U.S. Army CRREL**, Special Report #126.

Gow, A.J., 1963. *Results of measurements in the 309-meter bore hole at Byrd Station, Antarctica*. **Journal of Glaciology**, 4, 36.

Hammer, C.U., 1989. *Dating by physical and chemical seasonal variations and reference horizons*. In: **The Environmental Record in Glaciers and Ice Sheets**, eds., H. Oeschger and C.C. Langway, Jr., John Wiley and Sons, Limited, New York, 99-121.

Hammer, C.U., H.B. Clausen, and W. Dansgaard, 1980. *Greenland ice sheet evidence of post-glacial volcanism and its climatic impact*. **Nature**, 288, 230-235.

Hammer, C.U., H.B. Clausen, and H. Tauber, 1986. *Ice-core dating of the Pleistocene/Holocene boundary applied to a calibration of the $^{14}C$ time scale.* **Radiocarbon**, 28, 284-291.

Hammer, C.U., H.B. Clausen, W. Dansgaard, N. Gunderstrup, S.J. Johnsen, and N. Reeh, 1978. *Dating of Greenland ice cores by flow madels, isotopes, volcanic debris, and continental dust*. **J. of Glaciology**, 20, 3-26.

Hammer, C.U., H.B. Clausen, W. Dansgaard, A. Neftel, P. Kristindottir, and E. Johnsen, 1985. *Continuous impurity analysis along the Dye 3 deep core*. **In: Greenland Ice Core: Geophysics, Geochemistry, and Environment**, Geophys. Monog. 33, 90-94.

Herron, M.M., and C.C. Langway, Jr., 1985. *Chloride, nitrate, and sulfate in Dye 3 and Camp Century, Greenland ice cores*. **In: Greenland Ice Core: Geophysics, Geochemistry, and the Environment**, Geophys. Monog. 33, 77-84.

Hyde, W.T., T.J. Crowley, K.-Y. Kim, and G.R. North, 1989. *Comparison of GCM and energy balance model simulations of seasonal temperature changes over the past 18,000 years*. **J. Clim.**, 2, 864-887.

Imbrie, J. et al., 1984. *The orbital theory of Pleistocene climate: Support from a revised chronology of the marine $\delta^{18}O$ record.* **In: Milankovich and Climate**, 269-305.

Johnsen, S.J., 1977. *Stable isotope homogenization of polar firn and ice*. **In: Isotopes and impurities in snow and ice, Proc. IU66 Symp.**, 118, 210-219.

Johnsen, S.J., W. Dansgaard, and J. White, 1989. *The origin of Arctic precipitation under present and glacial conditions*. **Tellus**, 452-468.

Johnsen, S.J., W. Dansgaard, H.B. Clausen, and C.C. Langway, Jr., 1972. *Oxygen isotope profiles through the Antarctic and Greenland ice sheets*. **Nature**, 235, 429-434.

Jouzel, J. and Merlivat, L., 1984. *Deuterium and oxygen 18 in precipitation: modeling of the isotopic effect during snow formation*. **J. Geophys. Res.**, 89, 11749-11757.

Jouzel, J., G.L. Russell, R.J. Suozzo, R.O. Koster, J.W.C. White, and W.S. Broecker, 1987. *Simulations of the HDD and* $H_2^{18}O$ *atmospheric cycles using the NASA GISS general circulation model: the seasonal cycle for present day conditions.* **J. Geophys. Res.**, 92, 14739-14760.

Khalil, M.A.K. and R.A. Rasmussen, 1989. *Temporal variations of trace gases in ice cores.* In **The Environmental Record in Glaciers and Ice Sheets**, eds., H. Oeschger and C.C. Langway, Jr., John Wiley and Sons, Limited, New York, 193-205.

Kurtzbach, J.E., 1987. *Model simulations of the climatic patterns during the deglaciation of North America.* In: **North America and Adjacent Oceans During the Last Deglaciation**, Geological Society of America, Boulder, 425-446.

Langway, C.C., Jr., 1967. *Stratigraphic analysis of a deep ice core from Greenland.* **U.S. Army CRREL Research Report**, #77.

Lindstrom, D.R. and D.R. MacAyeal, 1989. *Scandinavian, Siberian, and Arctic ocean glaciation: Effect of Holocene atmospheric* $CO_2$ *variations.* **Science**, 245, 628-631.

Lorenz, E.N., 1967. *The Nature and Theory of the General Circulation.* **WMO Monograph**, 161.

Majoube, M., 1971. *Fractionnment en oxygen 18 et deuterium entre l'eau et sa vapour.* **J. Chim. Phy.**, 10, 1423-1436.

Manabe, S. and A.J. Broccoli, 1985. *A comparison of climate model sensitivity with data from the last glacial maximum.* **J. Atmos. Sci.**, 42, 2643-2651.

Manabe, S. and R.J. Stouffer, 1988. *Two stable equilibria of a coupled ocean-atmosphere model.* **J. Clim.**, 1, 841-866.

Merlivat, L. and J. Jouzel, 1979. *Global climatic interpretation of the deuterium-oxygen 18 relationship for precipitation.* **J. Geophys. Res.**, 84, 5029-5033.

Miller, R., 1983. **Continents in Collision.** *Planet Earth Series*, Time-Life Books, Alexandria, VA.

Morris, H.M., 1984. *The Biblical basis for modern science.* **Baker**, Grand Rapids, 516pp.

Morris, H. M., 1976. *The Genesis Record.* **Creation Life Publishers**, San Diego, 716pp.

Nicolis, C., 1984. *Self-oscillations, external forcings, and climate predictibility.* In: **Milankovitch and Climate**, D. Reidel, Dordrecht, Netherlands, 637-652.

Oard, M.J., 1990. *An ice age caused by the Genesis Flood.* **Institute for Creation Research Monograph**, San Diego, 243pp. - $19.95

Overgaard, S. and N. Gundestrup, 1985. *Bedrock topography of the Greenland ice sheet in the Dye 3 area.* In: **Greenland Ice Cores: Geophysics, Geochemistry, and Environment**, eds, C.C. Langway, Jr., H. Oeschger and W. Dansgaard, Geophys. Monog. 33, 44-56.

Petit, J.R., M. Briat, and A. Royer, 1981. *Ice age aerosol content from East Antarctic ice core samples and past wind strength.* **Nature**, 293, 391-394.

Petit, J.R., J.W.C. White, N.W. Young, J. Jouzel, and Y.S. Korotkevich, 1991. **J. Geophys. Res.**, 96, 5113-5122.

Petit, J.R., L. Mounier, J. Jouzel, Y.S. Korotkevich, V.I. Kotlyakov, and C. Lorius, 1990. *Palaeoclimatological and chronological implications of the Vostok core dust record.* **Nature**, 343, 56-58.

Pollard, D., 1978. *An investigation of the astronomical theory of the ice ages using a simple climate-ice sheet model.* **Nature**, 272, 233-235.

Pollard, D., A.P. Ingersoll, and J.G. Lockwood, 1980. *Response of a zonal climate-ice sheet model to the orbital perturbations during the Quaternary ice ages.* **Tellus**, 32, 301-319.

Ratcliffe, E.H., 1962. *The thermal conductivity of ice. New data on the temperature coefficient.* **Philosophical Magazine, eighth series**, 7, 1197-1203.

Rind, D., 1987. *Components of the ice age circulation.* **J. Geophys. Res.**, 92, 4241-4281.

Rind, D., D. Peteet, W. Broecker, A. McIntyre, and W. Ruddiman, 1986. *The impact of cold North Atlantic sea surface temperatures on climate: Implications for the Younger Dryas cooling (11-10K).* **Clim. Dynam.**, 1, 3-33.

Ruddiman, W.F. and A. McIntyre, 1981. *The North Atlantic Ocean during the last deglaciation.* **Palaeogeog., Palaeoclimatil., Palaeoecol.**, 35, 145-214.

Saltzman, B., 1985. *Paleoclimatic modeling.* In: **Paleoclimate Analysis and Modeling**, Wiley-Interscience, 341-396.

Saltzman, B., A. Sutera, and A. Evenson, 1981. *Structural stochastic stability of a simple auto-oscillatory climatic feedback system.* **J. Atmos. Sci.**, 38, 494-503.

Schwartz, S.E., 1988. *Are global cloud albedo and climate controlled by marine phytoplankton?* **Nature**, 336, 441-445.

Schytt, V., 1958. *Glaciology II: Scientific results of the Norwegian-British-Swedish Antarctic Expedition, 1949-1952.* **Oslo, Norsk Polarinstitutt**, 4, 7-148.

Scott, R.F., 1911. **Popperfoto**, London.

Sella, V., 1888. **Instituto di Fotografia Alpina**, Biella, Italy.

Sergin, V.Y., 1980. *Origin and mechanism of large-scale climatic oscillation.* **Science**, 209, 1477-1482.

Suarez, M.J. and I.M. Held, 1976. *Note on modeling climate response to orbital parameter variations.* **Nature**, 263, 46-47.

Suarez, M.J. and I.M. Held, 1979. *The sensitivity of an energy balance climate model to variations in the orbital parameters.* **J. Geophys. Res.**, 84, 4825-4836.

Ueda, H.T. and D.E. Garfield, 1968. *Drilling through the Greenland ice sheet.* **U.S. Army CRREL**, Technical Report #126, 7 pp.

Ueda, H.T. and D.E. Garfield, 1969. *Core drilling through the Antarctic ice sheet.* **U.S. Army CRREL**, Technical Report #231.

Ueda, H.T. and B.L. Hansen, 1967. *Installation of deep core drilling equipment at Byrd Station (1966-67).* **Antarctic Journal**, 2,4.

Ussher, J, 1786. **The Annals of the World**. Printed by E. Tyler for J. Crook and G. Bedell, London.

Weertman, J., 1976. *Milankovitch solar radiation variations and ice age ice sheet sizes.* **Nature**, 261, 17-20.

# APPENDIX

Special Report 126

# DRILLING THROUGH THE GREENLAND ICE SHEET

Herbert T. Ueda
and
Donald E. Garfield

November 1968

U.S. ARMY MATERIEL COMMAND
TERRESTRIAL SCIENCES CENTER
**COLD REGIONS RESEARCH & ENGINEERING LABORATORY**
HANOVER, NEW HAMPSHIRE

## PREFACE

This report was prepared by Mr. Herbert T. Ueda, Research Mechanical Engineer, and Mr. Donald E. Garfield, Mechanical Engineer, of the Technical Services Division, Cold Regions Research and Engineering Laboratory (CRREL), U.S. Army Terrestrial Sciences Center (USA TSC). The project was supervised by Mr. B. Lyle Hansen, Chief, Technical Services Division.

This report was originally prepared for and presented at the 12th Exploration Drilling Symposium, University of Minnesota, 22 Oct 1967.

Financial support was provided by the National Science Foundation. The U.S. Army Research Support Group supported the field operations.

The authors thank Mr. A. Arutunoff and Mr. T.K. Sutton of the Reda Pump Co. for their technical guidance and support of this project.

USA TSC is a research activity of the Army Materiel Command.

## CONTENTS



## ILLUSTRATIONS

**ABSTRACT**

In July 1966 a USA CRREL drilling team succeeded in penetrating the Greenland ice sheet at Camp Century, drilling through 4550 feet of ice and 12 feet of sub-ice material. The objectives of the project were to gain an understanding of the basic flow mechanism of large ice masses and to collect continuous, undisturbed cores for scientific analyses. The two techniques of core drilling used to complete the hole were thermal drilling and electrodrilling. This preliminary report describes the drilling equipment and techniques used at Camp Century from 1963 to the completion of the deep drill hole in 1966.

# DRILLING THROUGH THE GREENLAND ICE SHEET

by

Herbert T. Ueda and Donald E. Garfield

**Introduction**

In July 1966, a USA CRREL drilling team succeeded in penetrating the Greenland ice sheet at Camp Century after drilling through nearly a mile of ice. This effort, under the sponsorship of the National Science Foundation, was undertaken to gain an understanding of the basic flow mechanism of large ice masses such as the Greenland and Antarctic ice sheets and to provide continuous, undisturbed cores for scientific analyses (Bader, 1962).

The mechanism of ice sheet flow can best be determined from knowledge of the ice temperature, ice morainal content, and ice movement, each with respect to depth. This information can only be obtained by drilling a hole completely through the ice sheet, measuring the temperatures, retrieving and examining the cores, and measuring the deformation of the hole for a number of years afterward (Wagner, 1968).

The ice cores contain terrestrial and extraterrestrial materials that have fallen to the Earth's surface, in addition to samples of previous atmospheres in the form of tiny air bubbles. With methods now being developed for age dating the ice, the cores can become a new chronological source of geophysical and geochemical information extending back tens of thousands of years (Langway, 1967; Oeschger *et al.*, 1966).

This report describes the two techniques of core drilling used to complete the hole, thermal drilling and rotary drilling with the Electrodrill.

**Equipment and operations (thermal drill)**

The remoteness of the drilling sites and the normally short operating season in the polar regions precluded the use of conventional core drilling techniques (Lange, 1965). In an attempt to overcome these problems, an electrically heated, cable-suspended thermal drill was designed (Fig. 1).

The melting element was an annular copper heater, 6⅜ in. OD by 4⅞ in. ID,,with 18 cartridge heaters rated at 9 kilowatts. Spring-loaded core dogs, located just above the heater, were used to break off and retain the core. A 10-ft-long steel core barrel, a laminated plastic melt water collection tank, a switch housing, and a transformer comprised the remainder of the unit. A gear pump, located inside the melt water collection tank, pumped the water formed at the heater through heated nichrome tubes and up into the collection tank. The unit was 30 ft long and weighed 900 lb.

The drill was suspended from a 1-in.-diam. double armored electromechanical cable containing 12 electrical conductors. A hydraulic winch, with an attached 30-ft tower, was used to raise and lower the drill. Overall winch weight was 19 tons including 12,000 ft of cable. This unit was installed in an undersnow trench at Camp Century, Greenland (77° 10' N, 61° 08' W), about 140 miles east of Thule Air Base (Fig. 3).

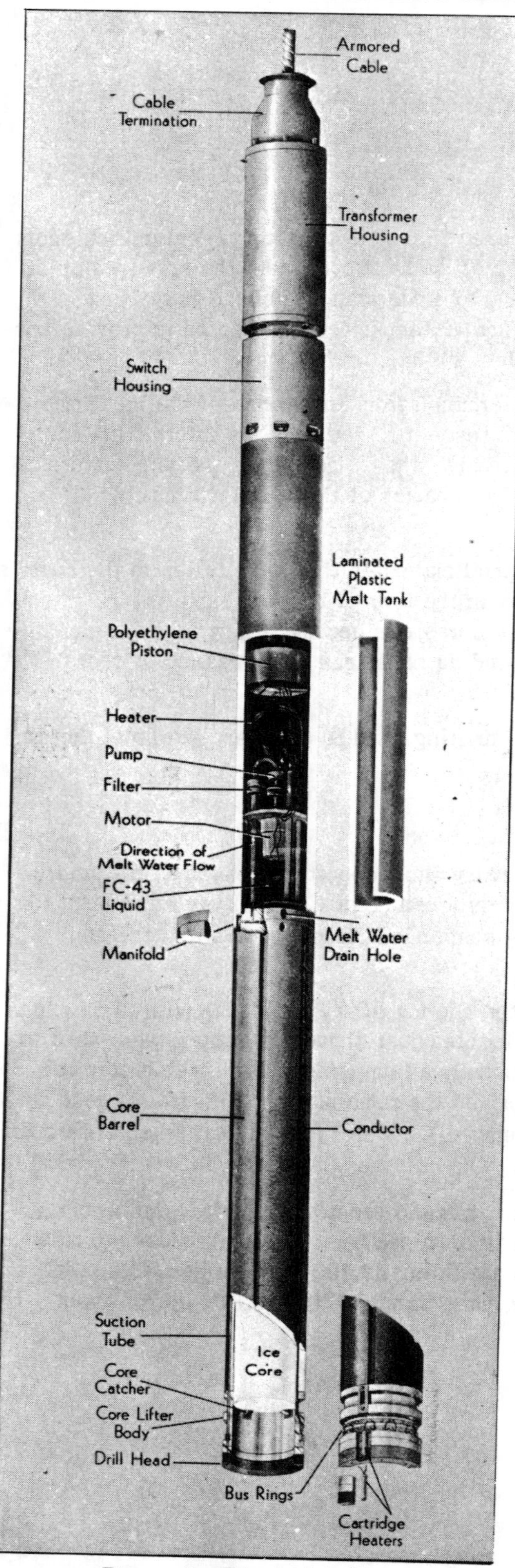


*Figure 1. Thermal drill.*

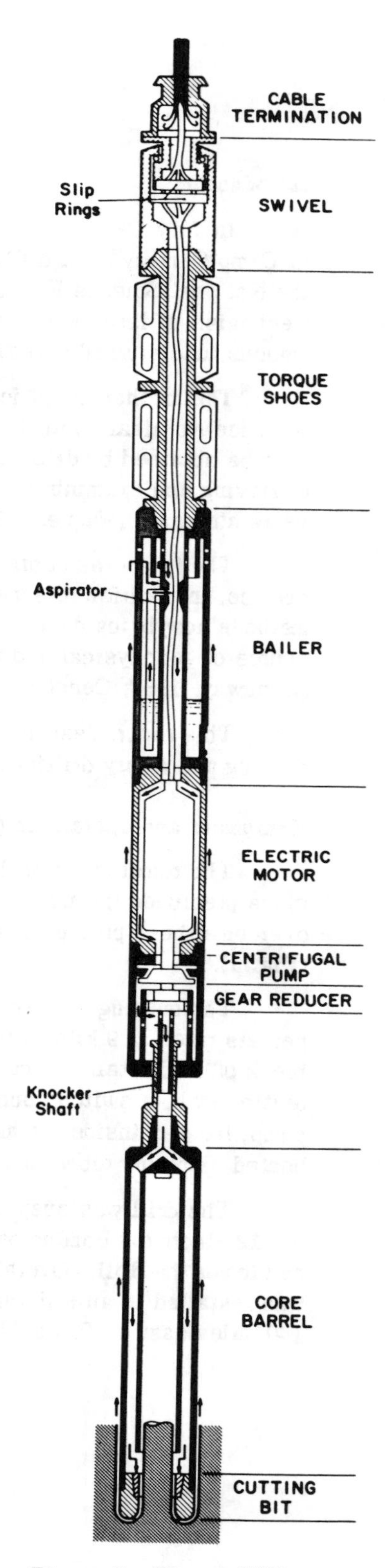


*Figure 2. Electrodrill.*

After two unsuccessful attempts to penetrate the ice sheet, a third hole was started in 1963 and advanced to 1755 ft by 1964, but not without difficulty. Drilling rates averaged about 1 in./min at power inputs of 5–6 kw and core recovery was 96%. Numerous problems were encountered. The most serious involved the removal and collection of melt water and the presence of residue in the hole which severely reduced the heat transfer, and subsequently the melting rate, of the heating element. Increasing the power did not increase the rate and only resulted in premature heater burnouts. Other problems included the breakage of electrical conductors within the cable, breakage of cable outer armor strands, and leaks in the winch hydraulic system.

To counteract hole closure caused by the plastic flow of the ice, the hole was loaded with a fluid of the same density as ice (0.92 g/cm$^3$). This fluid, a mixture of diesel oil and trichlorethylene, possessed strong solvent properties. It eventually removed a rust inhibiting compound used on the cable, creating a residue which continually settled to the bottom of the hole, impeded the melting rate, clogged the pumping circuit, and ultimately forced the discontinuation of drilling with the thermal method.

Further trials with the thermal drill in fluid-filled holes have not been pursued. However, for relatively shallow holes (less than 1500 ft) in clean ice, and where a fluid is not used in the hole, the thermal concept is feasible. In locations where a layer of permeable snow or firn must be penetrated before impermeable ice is reached, which is usually the condition encountered on the large ice sheets, thermal drilling is a very effective method. A unit for this purpose, the USA CRREL drill, has been developed (Ueda and Garfield, in press). This cable-suspended unit melts a hole $6\frac{7}{16}$ in. in diameter or larger and retrieves a core $4\frac{13}{16}$ in. in diameter or smaller, at a rate of $1\frac{1}{2}$ in./min with 3.5-4 kw of power. Gross weight of all necessary equipment is approximately 2400 lb including 1500 ft of cable.

**Equipment and operations (electrodrill)**

In 1964, a reconditioned electrodrill (Sutton and Arutunoff, 1954) was purchased and modified for use in ice. This cable-suspended, electromechanical rotary drill was invented by Mr. Armais Arutunoff, President of Reda Pump Co. of Bartlesville, Oklahoma.

The final version of the unit was 83 ft long and weighed 2650 lb. It consisted of six main sections (Fig. 2). At the top of the drill was a swivel section where the suspension cable terminated and where the electrical power was transmitted through a slip-ring assembly. This section allowed the rest of the drill to rotate relative to the cable. Below the swivel were the torque shoes which provided cutter reaction torque. Hinged shoes were designed to be thrown out against the hole wall and restrain the rotation of all but the core barrel and cutting bit. Problems with the slip rings eventually resulted in the elimination of the swivel section and it was discovered that cutter counter torque could be provided by the suspension cable alone without torque shoes. This technique of torque reaction was used throughout the remainder of the drilling.

The bailer was located just below the torque section and was modified for drilling in ice. In the original design the cuttings were deposited in the bottom of the bailer after being removed from the path of fluid flow. Since the density of the fluid in the hole was essentially equal to the ice chip density, this technique could not be used. Instead, the chips were dissolved in an aqueous ethylene glycol solution. This technique depends on a knowledge of the relationships shown in Figures 4 and 5, the freezing point diagram for aqueous ethylene glycol solutions (Cragoe, 1955) and the ice temperature versus depth profile for the location. A volume of concentrated glycol, the amount depending upon the downhole ice temperature and the volume of chips formed, is sent down in the bailer on each run. An aspirator assembly ensures mixing of the concentrated solution into the pump flow. This glycol dissolves the chips and dilutes itself to the equilibrium concentration for the downhole temperature. A bailer full of dilute solution is removed on each return trip with the core. Any solution remaining downhole will stay downhole since it is denser than, and immiscible with, the hole fluid. It will not melt any ice since it is

*Figure 3. Undersnow trench installation, Camp Century, Greenland.*

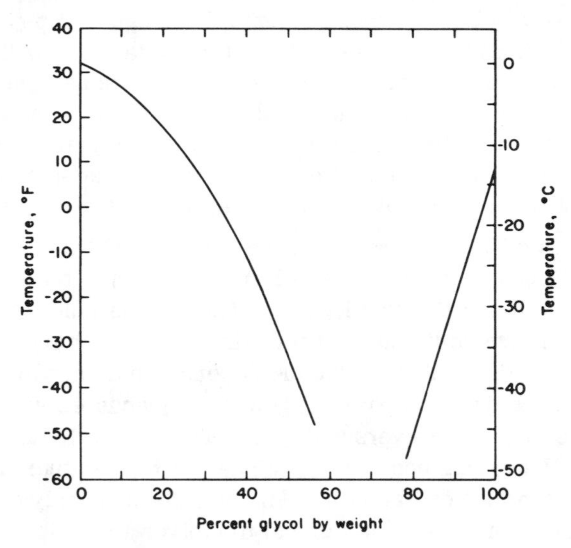


*Figure 4. Freezing points of aqueous ethylene glycol solutions (Cragoe, 1955).*

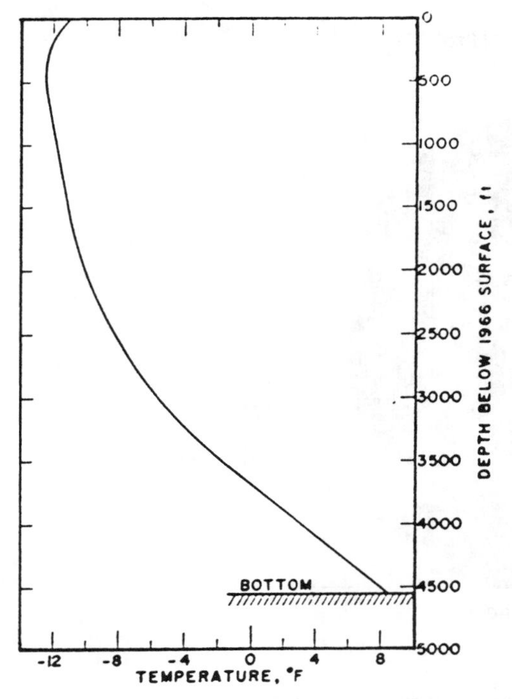


*Figure 5. Drill hole temperatures, Camp Century, 1966.*

at the equilibrium concentration. Glycol consumption is about 0.26 gal/ft of hole at 10F and 0.62 gal/ft at -20F. In ice colder than about -50F, the volume of glycol required makes the method logistically impractical.

In practice, more glycol was consumed, as the concentration of the solution was kept slightly rich. This resulted in some melting of the ice and subsequent downhole accumulation of solution. The excess was periodically removed, as its presence could prolong the period of time required for the hole to return to its original, undisturbed temperature. Approximate downhole temperatures were measured throughout the drilling.

Below the bailer was a 17½-hp, three-phase submersible induction motor, operated at 2300 v at a nominal speed of 3600 rpm. The glycol flowed through an annular space between the motor and its cylindrical housing. Heat from the motor, transferred to the glycol, provided the heat of solution to dissolve the ice chips.

Beneath the motor was a gear section which included a pump and gear reducer. The centrifugal pump was operated at 3600 rpm and rated at 80 gal/min with a 120-ft head. Below the pump, a planetary gear reducer dropped the shaft speed from 3600 rpm to 225 rpm, the speed of rotation of the core barrel and cutter.

Power was transmitted from the gear reducer to the core barrel through a splined hollow driveshaft. An 18-in. axial movement of the shaft allowed the core to be broken by impact if necessary. The core barrel was a double tube, swivel head type capable of holding a 20-ft core.

Two types of cutting bits with similar configurations were used, a steel bit with eight vertical mild steel inserts and a diamond bit with eight sintered tungsten carbide inserts (Fig. 6, 7). Diamonds were distributed around the outer face of each tungsten carbide insert with approximately 0.22 – 0.28 karats/stone and eight karats/insert. Bit dimensions were 6⅛ in. OD by 4½ in. ID. Core diameters averaged 4¼ in. or slightly less.

Aside from minor difficulties, drill performance was highly satisfactory. With a rotary speed of 225 rpm and approximately 700 lb of drill weight on the steel bit, drilling rates averaged 5–6 in./min with 11–12 kw of power. Less than 1 kw of power went into the cutting of the ice. By keeping the remaining drill weight in suspension, the hole was kept plumb. Equal drilling rates at lower bit loads were realized using the diamond bit. Eight- to fifteen-ft cores were retrieved in good condition using a tapered split-ring core lifter. Core recovery was 98%.

By July 1966 the hole was advanced from 1755 ft, where thermal drilling had been terminated, to the bottom of the ice sheet, 4450 ft from the surface. Coring continued to 4562 ft, where a worn bearing in the gear section prevented further penetration. Sub-ice material consisted of a conglomerate of frozen till and various sized rocks (Hansen and Langway, 1966). In this material, drill rates decreased to 1½ in./min and drill weight on the bit increased to 1800 lb with the power input rising to 16 kw.

*Figure 6. Diamond bit.*

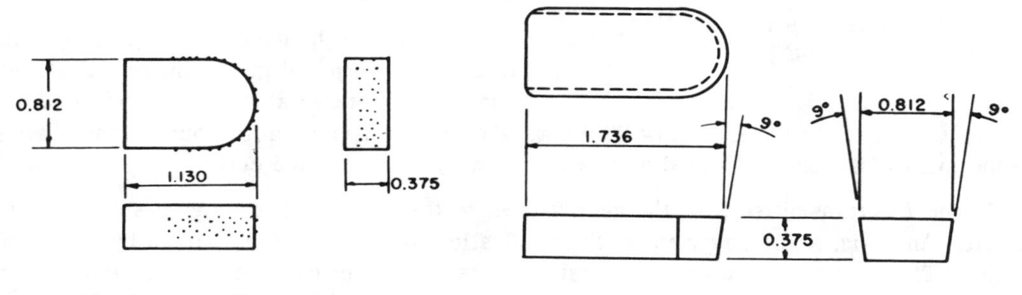


a. *Surface-set diamond insert.* b. *Mild steel insert.*

*Figure 7. Diamond and steel bit inserts.*

**Conclusions**

The feasibility of using a cable-suspended thermal drill or electrodrill for deep coring in ice has been demonstrated. The major problems encountered with the thermal drill were (1) the difficulty in designing a reliable melt water removal system when drilling in a fluid-filled hole, and (2) the requirement for a clean environment at the hole bottom. Neither of these problems affected the electrodrill and, in addition, the electrodrill penetrated faster. For core drilling deep holes in ice at temperatures higher than about -50F, the electrodrill with a steel or diamond bit, using the glycol chip removal concept, is the more desirable method.

**Literature cited**


Bader, H. (1962) Scope, problems, and potential value of deep core drilling in ice sheets. U.S. Army Cold Regions Research and Engineering Laboratory (USA CRREL) Special Report 58.

Cragoe, C.S. (1955) Properties of ethylene glycol and its aqueous solutions. National Bureau of Standards Report 4268.

Hansen, B.L. and Langway, C.C., Jr. (1966) Deep core drilling in ice and core analyses at Camp Century, Greenland, 1961–1966. *Antarctic Journal of the United States*, September – October, p. 207-208.

Lange, G.R. (in prep.) Deep rotary core drilling in ice. USA CRREL Technical Report 94.

Langway, C.C., Jr. (1967) Stratigraphic analysis of a deep ice core from Greenland. USA CRREL Research Report 77.

Oeschger, H.; Alder, B.; Loosli, H. and Langway, C.C., Jr. (1966) Radio-carbon dating of ice. *Earth and Planetary Science Letters*, vol. 1. p. 49-54.

Sutton, T.K. and Arutunoff, A. (1954) Use of electrodrill for oil well coring and drilling. Report prepared for presentation at the Petroleum Industry Electrical Conference of the American Institute of Electrical Engineering

Ueda, H.T. and Garfield, D.E. (in press) USA CRREL drill for thermal coring in ice. *Journal of Glaciology*.

Wagner, Lt. Col. J.E. (1968) Arctic ice cap. In *Yearbook of Science and Technology*. New York: McGraw Hill.